Zillions of Practice Problems

Fractions

Zillions of Practice Problems

Fractions

Stanley F. Schmidt, Ph.D.

Polka Dot Publishing

ISBN: 978-1-937032-56-2

Printed and bound in the United States of America

Polka Dot Publishing   Reno, Nevada

To order copies of books in the Life of Fred series,

visit our website PolkaDotPublishing.com

Questions or comments? Email the author at lifeoffred@yahoo.com

First printing

Zillions of Practice Problems Fractions was illustrated by the author with additional clip art
furnished under license from Nova Development Corporation, which holds the copyright to that art.

for Goodness' sake

or as J.S. Bach—who was
never noted for his plain
English—often expressed it:

Ad Majorem Dei Gloriam
(to the greater glory of God)

If you happen to spot an error that the author, the publisher, and the printer missed, please let us know with an email to: lifeoffred@yahoo.com

As a reward, we'll email back to you a list of all the corrections that readers have reported for this book.

What This Book Is All About

In the *Life of Fred: Fractions* book, there are *Your Turn to Play* sections in each lesson. And each *Your Turn to Play* offers complete solutions to each question.

One reason why teachers seem to know more than their students is that they have done many more problems than their students.

Students working through each lesson of *Life of Fred: Fractions* may do about a half dozen questions.

In Chapter 11, for example, we subtract fractions with the same bottoms. $\frac{7}{9} - \frac{5}{9} = \frac{2}{9}$ and $\frac{6}{13} - \frac{4}{13} = \frac{2}{13}$

How many of these would you have to do in order to figure out that you subtract the tops and copy the bottoms?

Some of my readers have written to me, "I want to know this fractions stuff like a teacher knows it. I want to know it well enough that I could stand in front of a classroom and do it."

Okay. I spent more than three months writing the book you now hold in your hands. *Zillions of Practice Problems Fractions* has about twice as many fractions problems as *Life of Fred: Fractions*.

Do all these and you should reach teacher-level.

HOW THIS BOOK IS ORGANIZED

Life of Fred: Fractions has 32 chapters. So does this book.

As you work through each chapter in *Life of Fred: Fractions* you can do the problems in the corresponding chapter in this book.

Each chapter in this book is divided into two parts.

★ The first part takes each topic and offers a zillion problems.
★ The second part is called the Mixed Bag. It consists of a variety of problems from the chapter and review problems from the beginning of the book up to that point.

HOW TO DO THE PROBLEMS

Get out paper and a pencil or pen. Do each problem. When you are done with this book, you will have a "book" of solutions written by you. This may be the first book you have ever written.

After you have written out your solution to a problem, then you may look at my solution. I have worked out each problem in detail in the back of the book.

The first question in this book is numbered "35." The second one is numbered "88." I didn't number them 1, 2, 3. . . . That would be foolish. When you looked up the answer to 1, you might accidentally see the answer to 2 and that would ruin the book you are writing.

❀   ❀   ❀

Fred is a teacher at KITTENS University. He is now 5½ years old. In this book and later books

Life of Fred: Decimals and Percents
Life of Fred: Pre-Algebras 0, 1, and 2
Life of Fred: Beginning Algebra Expanded Edition
Life of Fred: Advanced Algebra Expanded Edition
Life of Fred: Geometry Expanded Edition
Life of Fred: Trig Expanded Edition
Life of Fred: Calculus Expanded Edition

you will get to know four of Fred's students: Betty, Alexander, Darlene, and Joe.

Darlene and Joe are the funny ones. I've included lots of stories about them in this book.

8

Contents

Chapter One
Less Than

Problems from this chapter

35. Is $5\frac{1}{2} < 6$?

88. There are three ways people learn.
They are hearing, writing, and _____.
(fill in the blank with one word)

200. Add $772 + 857$.

444. < means "less than." > means "greater than."
      $4 < 11$ $11 > 4$
      Can you think of a way to remember which is which? Is there something about < that tells you the smaller number is on the left and the bigger number is on the right?

567. Suppose x is some number such that $x < 4$. What might x be equal to?

600. Fred can walk at 3 mph. On a bike he could go 10 mph. What does mph mean?

675. $83 \times 26 = ?$

733. If Fred wanted to go 65 mph, he wouldn't be able to do that on a bike. How could he go that fast?

820. Which of these are true and which are false?
      $8 < 5$
      $100 < 101$
      $30\frac{1}{2} < 40$

Chapter Two
A Billion

First part: Problems from this chapter

275. Which has the most eggs?
   A) Seven buckets, each holding eight eggs
   B) Nine lunch boxes, each holding six eggs
   C) Ten bags, each holding five eggs

300. 100 is said or written out as "one hundred."
   How would you say 6,000?
   How would you say 7,000,000,000?

420. If Fred could read three books in a week, how many could he read in 52 weeks?

100. Is 52 weeks less than a year? (There are approximately 365 days in a year.)

468. If every jar of peanuts contained 972 peanuts, how many peanuts would be in 8 jars?

556. Suppose we have a number. Let's call it x. Suppose we know that x > 6. A) Could x be equal to 3?
   B) Could x be equal to 4,754,984,681,613,005?
   C) Could x be equal to 6?

630. Onomatopoetic words sound like what they are describing. For example, water can *splash* or it can *drizzle* or it can *plop*.
   Your challenge: Write down as many onomatopoetic words as you can that begin with the letter C.

777. On March 27, 2016, Fred wanted to write a check to Cancer Research in the amount of $5,440. Help him fill out this check.
   (To answer this question, make a rough copy of this check and fill in the three blanks.)

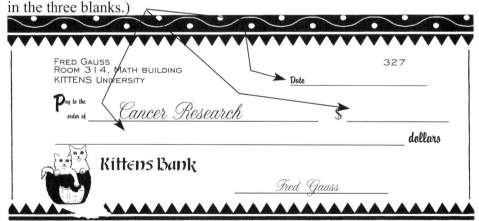

FRED GAUSS
ROOM 3 | 4, MATH BUILDING
KITTENS UNIVERSITY

327

Date

Pay to the
order of _____ *Cancer Research* _____ $ _____

_____ dollars

Kittens Bank

Fred Gauss

Second part: the 𝔐ixed 𝔅ag: a variety of problems from this chapter and the previous chapter

141. Fred can walk at 3 mph. In 5 hours he could walk 15 miles.
3 miles per hour × 5 hours = 15 miles.
How far could he walk in 4 hours?

325. Which of these are true and which are false?
  $7 < 96$
  $7 < 4$
  $7 < 6½$

475. 100 is said or written out as "one hundred."
How would you say 3,000?
How would you say 10,000?
How would you say 5,000,000?

650. Fred is shorter than Betty. Betty is shorter than Alexander.
Must it be true that Fred is shorter than Alexander?

225. Using what you learned from the answer to the previous problem,
is ≠ transitive?   ≠ means "not equal to."

513. A bunch of people are sitting on a long bench. Some of them are sitting right next to each other. Is "sitting right next to" transitive?

800. 72 × 58

Chapter Three
Cardinal and Ordinal Numbers

First part: Problems from this chapter

70. Fred is 36" tall and weighs 37 pounds. Draw a picture of what he would look like if he were 7' tall and still weighed 37 pounds.

234. Room number 234 would probably be on which floor of a building?

320. This is question 320. Is 320 a cardinal number or an ordinal number?

457. If you lined up the teachers at KITTENS University from shortest to tallest, Fred would be first in the line. Is first a cardinal number?

540. Fred has 16 pencils. How many more would he need in order to have a gross of pencils.   (Hint: one gross = 144.)

653. One gross of eggs is how many dozen eggs?

this picture
shows much
less than
144 eggs

723. The door to Fred's office is 78" tall. Since Fred is only 36" tall, he never hits his head on the top of the doorframe. He is thinking of getting a really tall hat. What is the tallest hat he could get and not have to duck when walking into his office?

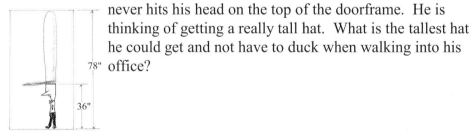

866. Change 78" into feet and inches. (Hint: Divide by 12 and any remainder will be the inches left over.)

Second part: the 𝔐ixed 𝔅ag: a variety of problems from this chapter and previous chapters

915. 68×78

595. 100 is said or written out as "one hundred."
How would you say 4,000,000?
How would you say 40,000?
How would you say 4,000,000,000?

250. Suppose we are looking at a bunch of sheep. Is "has more wool" transitive?

313. Which costs the most?
     A) Six chickens, each worth $7.
     B) Three dogs, each worth $13.
     C) Ten rats, each worth $3.

427. Fred could run at 7 mph. In 3 hours he could run 21 miles.
By the d = rt formula, $21 = 7 \times 3$.
     How far could Fred run in 8 hours? (We are assuming he doesn't get tired.)

689. If Fred bought a banana and put it in his desk drawer, it would spoil in 8 days.
     If Fred bought a dozen bananas and put them in his desk drawer, how long would it take for all those bananas to spoil?

583. Change 200" into feet and inches.

361. Does your calculator use ordinal numbers?

Chapter Four
Diameter and Radius

First part: Problems from this chapter

4. $\frac{2}{7} + \frac{3}{7} = ?$

68. Suppose a pizza had a 9" radius. Could you put a one-foot ruler on that pizza so that none of the ruler stuck out over the edge of the pizza? (One foot = 12")

204. Darlene told Joe, "If you were four times richer, you'd be worth $200." How much money does Joe have?

340. Name a number—let's call it x—so that 13 < x < 16.

526. Darlene has box that is 4' × 6'. What is the size of the largest round pizza that she could put in that box?

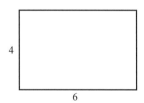

633. If a circle had a radius of 89 meters, what would be its diameter?
    (A meter is a little longer than a yard. A meter is in the metric system. A yard is in the imperial system.)

808. Darlene told Joe about a dream she had. She said, "I dreamed I was getting married to you, and we had the most beautiful white wedding cake."
    Joe said, "I like pizza better than cake. You can't have a white pizza."
    Darlene changed her story. "Okay. It was a big beautiful wedding pizza with all the toppings that you like on it."
    Joe thought for a moment and said, "I'd like $\frac{2}{5}$ of that pizza and you could have $\frac{1}{5}$ of it."
    How much of the pizza would they have?

Second part: the 𝔐ixed 𝔅ag: a variety of problems from this chapter and previous chapters

58. $\frac{3}{10} + \frac{4}{10} = ?$

64. 39×28

190. Could you put a circle with a diameter of 14 cm inside a circle with a radius of 9 cm?   (cm means centimeter. One cm is roughly the width of a fingernail.)

440. Which weighs the most?
     A) 9 five-ounce oranges
     B) 8 six-ounce peaches
     C) 4 eleven-ounce coconuts

495. If Fred could read and answer a piece of fan mail in 8 minutes,
how long would it take him to read and answer a dozen pieces of fan mail?

518. Fred could go 19 mph in his yacht.
How far could he go in 7 hours?

648. Change 314 minutes into hours and minutes. (Hint: To change minutes into hours you divide by 60. Any remainder will be leftover minutes.)

730. If Joe were four times stronger, he could lift 60 kg with his left arm.
How much could Joe lift with his left arm?
(kg means kilogram. A kilogram is a little over two pounds.)

870. Is it possible to name a number—let's call it x—so that 5 < x < 3?

Chapter Five
Fred's Budget

First part: Problems from this chapter

40. Joe likes jelly beans. If one bag of jelly beans cost $3, how much would ten bags cost?

133. Each month Joe spends $7 for fishing gear, $308 for rent, $93 for jelly beans, and $5 for food.

Each month Darlene spends $29 for nail polish, $47 for bridal magazines, $340 for rent.

Which of them spends more money?

209. Normally, Joe spends $93 each month for jelly beans. One month they went on sale and he saved $16. How much did Joe spend on jelly beans that month?

244. Fred makes $500 per month teaching at KITTENS University. He decides to spend one-fourth of his salary buying two-ounce bars of silver.

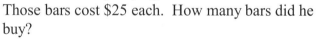

Those bars cost $25 each. How many bars did he buy?

303. (continuing the previous problem) Fred bought the silver bars hoping that the price would go up. It went up. He sold the bars for $75 each. How much did receive and what was his profit?

(Profit is how much you make after deducting your expenses. In this case it is the amount he received from selling minus the amount it cost him to buy the bars.)

349. On the day Fred bought the silver, he noticed that gold was 58 times more expensive than silver. A two-ounce bar of silver was $25. How much would a two-ounce bar of gold cost?

20

Second part: the 𝔐ixed 𝔅ag: a variety of problems from this chapter and previous chapters

680. 100 is said or written out as "one hundred."
How would you say 300,000,000?
How would you say 47,000?
How would you say 97,000,000,000?

52. Change 198 minutes into hours and minutes.

381. Your piggy bank has 39,741 pennies in it. (It's a big piggy bank.)
Is 39,741 a cardinal or an ordinal number?

125. $\frac{5}{9} + \frac{2}{9} = ?$

480. Name a number—let's call it x—so that
400 < x < 900.

590. Darlene has a 3' × 8' rug in her bathroom. Joe wanted to cut a circle out of that rug that was as large as possible. How big could that circle be?

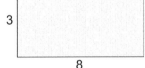

You might be curious why Joe wanted to cut a circle out of Darlene's bathroom rug. Darlene was also curious. While Joe was cutting up her rug, Darlene asked him. He said that there was a big round hole in the bottom of his fishing boat and he wanted to cover that hole.
          Darlene screamed, "That won't stop a leak!"
          Joe said "I never thought of that."

740. If the diameter of a circle is 740, what would be its radius?

786. Darlene normally spends $29 each month for nail polish. One month the price of nail polish went up and she had to spend $47 instead. How much more money did she have to spend that month on nail polish?

900. If regular jelly beans cost 7 cents each, and if Texas-sized jelly beans cost 38 times as much, how much would a Texas-sized jelly bean cost?

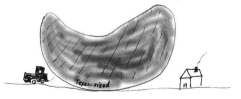

Chapter Six
Doubling

First part: Problems from this chapter

14. Fred planted a bean. Later that month it was 37" tall. In another week it doubled in height. How tall was it then?

60. If doubling means multiplying by 2, what does tripling mean?

130. Joe liked Fred's bean plant. Joe asked Fred, "What kind of beans can you plant?"

Fred said, "There are many different beans. For example, there are adzuki beans, anasazi beans, black beans, borlotti beans, butter beans, cannellini beans, chestnut lima beans, corona beans, fava beans, flageolet beans, garbanzo beans, chana dal beans, great northern beans, kidney beans, lima beans, lupini beans, marrow beans, moth beans, mung beans, navy beans, pink beans, pinto beans, red beans, scarlet runner beans, soybean beans, tepary beans, and urad beans."

Joe wasn't very good at paying attention. His mind wandered. By the time Fred got to butter beans, Joe was opening his bag of jelly beans and eating them by the handful. He was sure that jelly beans was on Fred's list.

Joe planted a jelly bean. It was June 1st. On June 2nd he planted 2 jelly beans. Then 4 jelly beans on June 3rd. Then 8 jelly beans on June 4th.

He continued. How many did he plant on June 11th?

206. Normally, Joe would spend $93 each month on jelly beans. In June his jelly bean costs tripled because he was planting so many jelly beans. What was his jelly bean cost in June?

401. When you double the height of a child (or a moose or a tree or a house) you increase its weight by about eightfold.

If a three-foot tall dog weighed 29 pounds, what would its expected weight be when it was six-feet tall?

Second part: the 𝔐ixed 𝔅ag: a variety of problems from this chapter and previous chapters

150. $\frac{5}{17} + \frac{8}{17} = ?$

290. 87×76

470. Which has the greatest volume?
    A) Seven garbage cans, each holding 6 gallons
    B) Ten garbage cans, each holding 5 gallons
    C) Five garbage cans, each holding 9 gallons.

543. When Joe was out fishing in his boat, he once accidentally dropped a purple jelly bean into the water. Joe liked purple jelly beans because they made his tongue purple.
    This jelly bean made the water around the boat purple. Forty feet in every direction the water was purple. What was the diameter of that purple circle?

610. Suppose we are looking a bunch of telephones. Is "older than" transitive?

720. If Joe could eat a 2-pound bag of jelly beans in 6 minutes, why would it be silly to say he could eat twelve 2-pound bags of jelly beans in 72 minutes?

727. At KITTENS University the teachers' monthly salaries total $83,938. The president's salary is $197,668. The janitors' salaries total $3,077. What is the total monthly salaries for all these people?

781. Alexander is 73" tall. How much is that in feet and inches?

(Continued next page)

284. Ants were everywhere in Joe's apartment. At the hardware store they told Joe to buy ant poison. He didn't like that idea. Instead, he went to a pet store. They suggested getting an anteater. It would cost $79, and they could get it in a week. Joe told them he needed it right now. They said they could they get it by this afternoon, but a special order would increase the cost sevenfold. Joe said, "Yes." How much would the anteater cost Joe?

First part: Problems from this chapter

43. Draw a circle and divide it into three equal sectors.

91. Find the sum of seven, fifteen, and fifty-nine.

103. Which is smaller: $\frac{1}{3}$ or $\frac{1}{4}$?

164. $7 \times 8 = ?$
    $0 \times 6 = ?$
    $3,782,981,552 \times 0 = ?$

197. Write in words 3,782,981,552.

212. Darlene watched 111 minutes of television while she was painting her toenails. One-third of that time was commercials. How many minutes were those commercials?

248. Is one billion $\geq$ one million?

310. Think of a number. Call that number x. Is it true that $x < x + 1$?

370. Fred had $1,935.06 in his checking account. He wrote a check for $1,935.06. How much did Fred have left in his account?

451. Fred was whistling as he walked home after buying his bicycle.

    He whistled 88 notes every minute. It took him seven minutes to walk home. How many notes did he whistle on that trip?

    Note that the word *whistle* has a silent *t* in it. English is harder than math.

Second part: the 𝕸ixed 𝕭ag: a variety of problems from this chapter and previous chapters

188. Fred could fly in his jet at 778 mph.
How far could he go in 8 hours?
Recall: distance equals rate times time. d = rt

240. When Joe was fishing in his boat, he played his radio so loudly that all the fish in the water near him died.

An airplane flew over Joe and saw of circle of dead fish that was 300 feet in diameter. How far away could Joe's radio kill fish? (In other words, what was the radius of that circle?)

279. Darlene liked to read bridal magazines. One article said that for a cheap wedding you should expect to spend $786 for dresses, $655 for music, $88 for invitations, and $19 to rent the groom's tuxedo. The food for the reception is another $2484.

How much is this wedding going to cost?

367. (continuing the previous problem) Darlene saves $12/month. How many months will she have to save to afford her wedding?

453. (continuing the previous problem) How many years will she have to save?

577. Think of a number. Call that number x. Is it always true that x ≤ x?

607. In symbols, *x is less than 50* is written x < 50.
How would you write in symbols *y is greater than or equal to 8*?

638. Joe bought eight anteaters.

They dined on 448 ants and shared them equally. Anteaters are very nice and like to share. How many ants did each anteater get?

Chapter Eight
Comparing Fractions

First part: Problems from this chapter

215. Draw a circle with three equal sectors. Color in $\frac{2}{3}$

322. Which is true: $\frac{2}{3} < \frac{3}{4}$ or $\frac{3}{4} < \frac{2}{3}$? (Drawing two circles and coloring in two-thirds of one of them and three-fourths of the other may help.)

363. This Fred's current teaching schedule.

8:00 A.M.	BEGINNING ALGEBRA
9:00 A.M.	ADVANCED ALGEBRA
10:00 A.M.	GEOMETRY
11:00 A.M.	TRIG
12 M.	CALCULUS
1:00 P.M.	TRIP TO THE LIBRARY

What fraction of his classes does he teach before noon?

502. Is $\frac{1}{6}$ less than $\frac{1}{4}$?

547. One-fourth of Joe's weight is fat. If he weighed 160 pounds, how much fat is he carrying around?

578. There are 24 hours in a day. Fred spends one-twelfth ($\frac{1}{12}$) of each day reading. How long is that?

Second part: the 𝔐ixed 𝔅ag: a variety of problems from this chapter and previous chapters

194. $\frac{1}{5} + \frac{2}{5} = ?$

218. Fred went to the library and checked out 7 pounds of astronomy books, 28 pounds of physics books, 38 pounds of history books, 13 pounds of poetry books, 45 pounds of math books, and 34 pounds of business books.

   He couldn't carry all those books so he sent them by campus mail. The mailman left them on top of his desk. His desk already had a flowerpot (with tulips) on it that weighed 4 pounds. Fred's desk could support 170 pounds without breaking. Would the desk break?

430. 97×47

550. Joe had a nightmare that the price of jelly beans quadrupled. (That means it increased fourfold.) Joe's favorite are fish-flavored jelly beans. They were 29¢ each. How much would they be after the price increase?

790. 100 is said or written out as "one hundred."
How would you say 243?
How would you say 45,000,000,000?
How would you say 237,000,000?

818. Think of a number. Call that number x. Could it ever be true that x = x + 3?

905. Four-fifths ($\frac{4}{5}$) of Joe's diet comes from sugar. The rest of it comes from the starch in french fries. Draw a rectangle and color in four-fifths of it.

   Once Joe, Darlene, Betty, Alexander, and Fred went out to a hamburger place together. Joe complained that the french fries weren't sweet enough.

   Alexander watched in horror as Joe poured some sugar on the table, licked a french fry and rolled it in the sugar.

   Joe's diet may greatly increase his chances of heart disease, cancer, and diabetes.

Chapter Nine
Reducing Fractions

First part: Problems from this chapter

207. Fred's gift to Alexander was an 18" knife. A sword can be a yard long. (1 yard = 36") The length of that knife is what fraction of the length of a sword? Please reduce your answer as much as possible.

238. Betty, Alexander, and Joe ordered a Gallon-size™ carton of french fries at Handy Harry's Hamburgers.

It contained 537 fries.
If they shared it equally, how many fries would Joe receive?

286. Reduce $\dfrac{100}{150}$

355. Darlene suggested that Joe come with her on a walk in the Great Woods near the KITTENS campus.

Joe asked, "Where are we going?"

Darlene answered, "We are just going walking. We can see some flowers and some butterflies."

Joe said, "You mean some nature stuff."

Joe packed 56 bags of jelly beans in his backpack. On the one-hour walk, he ate 21 of those bags. What fraction had he eaten? Please reduce your answer as much as possible.

376. Joe had 21 empty jelly bean bags. He took one of them and blew it up, twisted the end, and popped it by clapping his hands together.

This frightened the birds in the trees. They flew away.

He did it twice more.

What fraction of the empty bags had he popped?

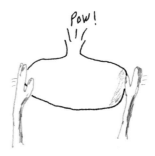

Second part: the 𝔐ixed 𝔅ag: a variety of problems from this chapter and previous chapters

230. $\frac{4}{15} + \frac{7}{15} = ?$

353. Think of a number. Call that number x. Is it always true x + 7 = 7 + x?

395. If Joe had popped 3 of the 21 empty bags, what fraction of the empty bags had he not popped?

450. Room 765 is probably on which floor of a building?

461. Joe spends $413 each month. Each month his mother gives him $43. He gets $293 from the government. He gets $8 from selling fish. He gets $69 from waving a sign in front of Stanthony's pizza place.
   How much will Joe save each month?
   How much will he save each year?
   How much will he save in a century?

552. Do $\frac{9}{12}$ and $\frac{75}{100}$ reduce to the same fraction?

816. Darlene made a cherry pie.
She sliced it into eight equal sectors.
(One for her, one for her mom, one for Betty, one for Alexander, one for Joe, and three more for Joe if he wanted extra pieces.) Draw a picture of Darlene's slices.

935.   100 is said or written out as "one hundred."

How would you say 644?
How would you say 5,000,733?
How would you say 2,920?

Chapter Ten
Add and Reduce

First part: Problems from this chapter

216. $\frac{1}{5} + \frac{2}{5} = ?$

306. $\frac{7}{31} + \frac{8}{31} = ?$

327. Darlene owns 56 bottles of nail polish. Twenty-eight of them are red. What fraction of her nail polish bottles are red? (Remember to reduce your answer if that's possible.)

351. On one fishing trip Joe caught 4 salmon and 16 guppies.

What fraction of his catch were guppies?

424. (continuing the previous problem) Salmon weigh a lot more than guppies. If each of the salmon Joe caught weighed 9 pounds, and each of the guppies weighed one ounce, then . . .

    A) How much did all the salmon weigh?

    B) How many pounds did the guppies weigh? (one pound = 16 ounces)

    C) What was the total weight of his catch?

    D) What fraction of the total weight were the guppies?

Second part: the 𝔐ixed 𝔅ag: a variety of problems from this chapter and previous chapters

55. Change 63" to feet and inches.

69. Darlene read in one of her bridal magazines that if you hold your wedding in New York City rather than in Kansas, the total price will triple. She had estimated that marrying Joe in Kansas would cost about $7849. How much would that cost in New York City?

255. $\frac{3}{8} + \frac{3}{8} = ?$

378. Here is Fred's drawing of a pony.

      Fred's doll, Kingie, drew a picture of that same pony. Kingie can draw a lot better than Fred can.

      Kingie's picture sold for $602. Fred's picture sold for one-seventh of what Kingie's picture sold for.

      What was the selling price of Fred's picture?

652. 200 ounces is how many pounds. (16 ounces = 1 pound)

735. Joe was given this problem: **Suppose x is cardinal number and suppose that 40 < x < 42. What is x?**

    Joe wanted to be fancy and wrote $40\ \frac{7}{8}$

    The teacher said his answer was wrong. Why?

Chapter Eleven
Subtracting Fractions with the Same Denominators

First part: Problems from this chapter

252. $\dfrac{9006}{9888} - \dfrac{7847}{9888} = ?$

294. Stanthony is the owner of PieOne—the best pizza place near KITTENS University. When he was born, his parents named him Stanley Anthony. As a baby his first solid food was pizza.

In elementary school everyone called him Stanthony. His lunch box always had a pizza in it.

In high school all his work dealt with pizza.

✳ In English class, he wrote a poem: **O pizza, how I love thee.**
Let me count the ways.

✳ In history class he wrote a history of the wars about pizzas. (Italy won.)

✳ In art class he renamed all the colors: red ➠ tomato red

green ➠ green pepper green

brown ➠ pizza crust

light yellow ➠ mozzarella

✳ In math every problem in fractions became a problem of cutting a pizza into equal slices.

Start with a really big pizza and cut it into 18 equal slices. If 6 of the slices are eaten, what fraction of the pizza is left?

317. One of Stanthony's really big pizzas is cut into 18 equal slices. Each slice weighs 7 pounds. How much does the whole pizza weigh?

357. A dump truck would deliver the mozzarella cheese to the back of PieOne. To make a really big pizza, Stanthony shoveled $\dfrac{3}{19}$ of the cheese

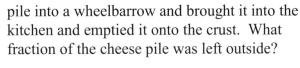

pile into a wheelbarrow and brought it into the kitchen and emptied it onto the crust. What fraction of the cheese pile was left outside?

Second part: the 𝔐ixed 𝔅ag: a variety of problems from this chapter and previous chapters

92. I'm thinking of a number. I'll call that number x.
It is true that x + 7 = 12. What number am I thinking of?

281. $\frac{1}{8} + \frac{5}{8} = ?$

345. Two-sevenths of Joe's boat is filled with fishing equipment. One-seventh of the boat is filled with bottles of Sluice. Three-sevenths of the boat is filled with bags of jelly beans. How much of his boat is occupied by fishing equipment, Sluice, and jelly beans?

560. 99 × 57

586. Darlene imagines that her wedding cake will weigh 296 pounds. One-eighth of it will be frosting. How many pounds will the frosting weigh?

658. (continuing the previous problem) If Joe ate all the frosting, what fraction of the cake would be left?

685. After eating 37 pounds of frosting, Joe would weigh 185 pounds. What fraction of his body would be frosting?

725. Darlene had planned an 84-day honeymoon with Joe. If Joe ate 37 pounds of frosting, he would spend one-twelfth of those 84 honeymoon days in the hospital. How many days of their honeymoon would be lost?

Chapter Twelve
Common Denominators

First part: Problems from this chapter

213. $\dfrac{5}{8} = \dfrac{?}{24}$

242. $\dfrac{3}{4} = \dfrac{27}{?}$

296. Compare $\dfrac{3}{5}$ and $\dfrac{14}{20}$

321. Compare $\dfrac{3}{4}$ and $\dfrac{2}{3}$

365. What's the least common denominator for $\dfrac{1}{15}$ and $\dfrac{1}{20}$?

416. What's the least common denominator for $\dfrac{1}{18}$ and $\dfrac{1}{180}$?

446. The least common denominator of $\dfrac{1}{360}$ and $\dfrac{1}{150}$ is 1,800.

What is the least common denominator of $\dfrac{7}{360}$ and $\dfrac{117}{150}$?

504. What is the least common denominator for fractions whose denominators are 4, 6, and 10?

598. Darlene had packed a zillion cherries for a picnic with Joe.

Joe said that he would be happy with $\dfrac{5}{8}$ of the cherries.

Darlene was on a diet and said she would be happy with $\dfrac{1}{3}$ of them. They both agreed that they would feed the rest of them to the duck.

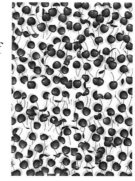

The duck suggested that they get a bunch of plastic bags and divide the zillion cherries equally into the bags. How many bags should they use so that Joe could take $\dfrac{5}{8}$ of the bags and Darlene could take $\dfrac{1}{3}$ of the bags?

Second part: the 𝔐ixed 𝔅ag: a variety of problems from this chapter and previous chapters

11. Joe got a job as a sign waver in front of Stanthony's PieOne Pizza. He worked 3 hours per day for 17 days and was paid $8 per hour.

    The government took one-third of his pay in income taxes. How much did Joe have left?

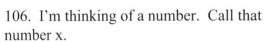

106. I'm thinking of a number. Call that number x.

It is true that 6x = 42. What is that number?

    6x means "six times x."

288. $\frac{4}{15} + \frac{4}{15} = ?$

329. Which is smaller: $\frac{7}{9}$ or $\frac{9}{11}$?

432. What's the least common denominator for $\frac{1}{10}$ and $\frac{1}{15}$?

472. What is the least common denominator for fractions whose denominators are 5, 10, and 15?

591. Darlene spent her Saturday reading bridal magazines. (She leaves her college work until Sunday evening.) She started reading at 8 a.m. and finished at 3 p.m. She took a 17-minute break for lunch. How many minutes did she read?

660. One of Darlene's magazines said that $\frac{1}{5}$ of your wedding budget should be for the wedding gown, $\frac{1}{3}$ for the wedding reception, and $\frac{1}{15}$ for photography. What fraction of the budget do these three items consume?

744. Darlene imagined spending $870 for her wedding flowers. There would be her magnificent bridal bouquet, flowers for the six bridesmaids, and a six-dollar plastic flower for Joe's coat.

    Six dollars is what fraction of $870?

Chapter Thirteen
Roman Numerals

First part: Problems from this chapter

223. Write the Roman numerals from 21 to 30.

241. Write the Roman numerals for 70, 90, and 2,000.

257. The letter *I* can only go to the left of *V* or *X* (to indicate subtraction).
The letter *X* can only go to the left of ? or ? .
The letter *C* can only go to the left of ? or ? .

308. Doing arithmetic in Roman numerals is very difficult. It's a little like trying to translate into Latin words like *proton* or *television*.
    If you have to multiply LXXVII by VII, the easiest way to first convert the numerals into Arabic numerals, then do the multiplication, and then convert back into Roman numerals.
    Do it.

331. Divide MMMMCXVI by LXXXIV and express your answer in Roman numerals.

372. It is hard to do arithmetic in Roman numerals. It is also hard to express larger numbers in Roman numerals.
    A university professor might make $90,000 per year. (This is not Fred. He makes $500/month, which is $6,000/year.) How would you write 90,000 in Roman numerals?

548. You can't write *IM* for 999 because *I* can only go in front of *V* or *X*.
    How would you write 999 in Roman numerals?

There are a couple reasons why the Romans wouldn't have had calculators like this one.

1. They didn't have plastic.
2. They didn't have electricity.

Second part: the 𝔐ixed 𝔅ag: a variety of problems from this chapter and previous chapters

95. I'm thinking of a number. Call that number x. It is true that $7x = 56$. What is that number?   7x means "seven times x."

228. Divide MMLXXXVIII by XXIX. Express your answer in Roman numerals.

237. $\dfrac{13}{30} + \dfrac{14}{30} = ?$

246. When Joe and Darlene went to the movies, Joe liked to order popcorn.

"The problem with popcorn," Joe explained, "is that it's so boring." Joe would sit there eating the kernels one by one and counting, "One popcorn, two popcorns, three popcorns. . . ."

Darlene told Joe that she couldn't hear the movie and asked him to count silently.

To make the popcorn more exciting, Joe would stir jelly beans into his box of popcorn. For every six kernels of corn he would add one jelly bean. Three thousand four hundred sixty-eight kernels of popcorn would require how many jelly beans?

298. Which is smaller: $\dfrac{2}{3}$ or $\dfrac{13}{20}$?

482. What is the least common denominator for fractions whose denominators are 2, 4, 6, 8, and 10?

497. What is the least common denominator for fractions whose denominators are IX and XV? Give your answer in Roman numerals.

794. If Joe had 4,775 jelly beans, how many more would he need to have a million jelly beans?

Chapter Fourteen
Adding Fractions

First part: Problems from this chapter

222. Darlene had packed a zillion cherries for a picnic with Joe.

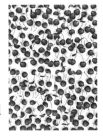

Joe said that he would be happy with $\frac{5}{8}$ of the cherries.

Darlene was on a diet and said she would be happy with $\frac{1}{3}$ of them. They both agreed that they would feed the rest of them to the duck. What fraction of the cherries would the people get?

283. Joe had counted all the cherries before they divided them up. Darlene had packed 240 cherries. Darlene was going to get one-third of the cherries. How many was that?

This is the same as asking $\frac{1}{3} = \frac{?}{240}$

333. Darlene had packed 240 cherries. Joe was going to get five-eighths of them. How many was that?

422. On the picnic Darlene spent a third of her time handing Joe cherries. She spent one-third of her time explaining to Joe that he should spit the cherry pits into a garbage bag she had brought.

She even wrote a sign on the side of the bag.

Joe tried to remember. But sometimes he forgot and spit the pits on the ground.

Darlene spent one-sixth of her time picking up the pits and putting them into the bag.

After she spent $\frac{1}{3}$ of her time handing cherries, $\frac{1}{3}$ of her time explaining, and $\frac{1}{6}$ of her time picking up pits, how much time did she have left?

Second part: the 𝔐ixed 𝔅ag: a variety of problems from this chapter and previous chapters

101. Think of a number. Call that number x. Is it always true that $x + 0 = x$?

247. Darlene also packed a big cherry pie for Joe on their picnic. She cut it into 12 equal pieces. Joe said he wanted one-third of the pie. How many pieces was that?

425. What's the least common denominator for $\frac{1}{16}$ and $\frac{1}{32}$?

486. IX Romans found CCCXXXIII gold pieces and divided the coins equally among them. How many gold pieces did each Roman receive? Give your answer in Roman numerals.

545. Is the number of Roman soldiers in the previous problem a cardinal number or an ordinal number?

593. 287 inches is how many yards and inches? (36 inches = 1 yard)

640. Now a problem in the metric system. 600 centimeters is how many meters? (100 centimeters = 1 meter)   You do the same thing as in the previous problem.

691. Is this true: $\frac{5}{6} < \frac{7}{8}$?

Chapter Fifteen
Fractions Mean Divide

First part: Problems from this chapter

249. A fifth of an hour is how many minutes?

282. Darlene was planning a birthday party for herself. She ordered 167 liters of Sluice, which was to be served to her 644 guests. If all the guests received the same amount, how much would each receive?

318. Darlene estimated that half of her 644 birthday party guests would bring her gifts that were worth over $300 each. How many of these gifts worth more than $300 did she expect to receive?

334. Darlene sent out 644 birthday party invitations. The invitations were on postcards rather than in envelopes in order to save money. Many of the people looked at the postcards and asked, "Who is this Darlene?" They tossed the postcard into the garbage. This was because she had sent invitations to everyone she could think of, including the Kansas senators, the local dog catcher, and members of the Jeanette MacDonald fan club.

Six hundred thirty-six invited people weren't going to her birthday party. What fraction would be attending?

558. Darlene hired a band to play at her birthday party. Each rabbit charged $8. How much would the four-rabbit band cost?

603. Darlene, of course, invited Joe to her party. He brought along a bag of jelly beans in case there wasn't enough to eat at the party. It was a 15-pound bag and contained 3,708 jelly beans. (Joe had counted them.) The bag got heavy, and Joe set it down. The four rabbits thought it was a tip for their wonderful dancing, singing, and horn playing. They shared it equally among themselves. How many jelly beans did each rabbit get?

41

Second part: the 𝔐ixed 𝔅ag: a variety of problems from this chapter and previous chapters

7. Name a number—let's call it x—so that $15 < x < 16$.

219. Which is smaller: $\dfrac{11}{12}$ or $\dfrac{15}{18}$?

359. Joe caught 88 fish. Three-fourths of them had blue fins. How many was that?

484. Joe had caught LXXXVIII fish. He could sell them for VII¢ each. How much could he get for those fish? (¢ means cents.)

506. Those 88 fish had eaten 11 pounds of bait before they were caught. If all the fish had eaten the same amount, how much did each fish eat?

563. Think of a number. Call that number y.
Suppose you know that $y + 9 = 23$. What is the value of y?

655. A pound equals 16 ounces. If each fish ate $\dfrac{1}{8}$ of a pound of bait, how many ounces would that be?

710. It takes Joe 26 minutes to dig up a pound of worms. How long would it take him to dig up 11 pounds?

737. Change 286 minutes into hours and minutes.

783. Joe liked to fish, but he didn't enjoy eating fish. "They aren't sweet enough," he would say.
    Once he tried to make a fish milkshake. His recipe was:

3 fish
36 ounces of sluice
1 drop of milk

    He put it in the blender for ten minutes. He poured one-fifth of it into his milkshake mug. How much fish was in that mug?

Chapter Sixteen
Least Common Multiple

First part: Problems from this chapter

338. Find the least common multiple (LCM) of 3, 6, and 9.

360. What is the LCM of 4, 8, and 16?

392. When I want to add $\frac{1}{4}$ and $\frac{2}{5}$ do I need to find the LCM of 1 and 2 or do I need to find the LCM of 4 and 5?

429. $\frac{1}{4} + \frac{2}{5} = ?$

515. Darlene is planning her wedding reception dinner. She wants to order special dinner plates with "D & J" printed on each plate. These plates can only be ordered in groups of 8.

Darlene doesn't want to waste plates, so she wants to have the total number of people attending (including herself and Joe) to be 8 or 16 or 24 or 80 or. . . . The number attending should be divisible by 8.

She also wants each person (including herself and Joe) to receive a special fish mug. She knew that Joe would think that they were in honor of his fishing talents. In reality Darlene was thinking, "I caught him." The fish mugs can only be ordered in multiples of 10.

What is the smallest number that can attend the wedding reception dinner without wasting plates or mugs?

Second part: the 𝕸ixed 𝕭ag: a variety of problems from this chapter and previous chapters

335. Think of a number. Call that number x.
Suppose you know that x – 7 = 14. What is the value of x?

374. $\frac{1}{3} + \frac{3}{5}$ = ?

418. The least common denominator for $\frac{1}{28}$ and $\frac{1}{42}$ is 84.

What is the least common multiple of 28 and 42?

554. Joe eats jelly beans by the handful. Over the years he has discovered

that the best flavor balance is 4 fire red beans, 6 orange beans, and 7 vanilla beans. He puts these 17 beans in his hand, throws them into his mouth, chews hard, and swallows. The whole process takes 4 seconds.
    How many handfuls could Joe eat in a minute?

620. If there are 360° in a circle, how many degrees are in a quarter of a circle?

664. Which number is smaller: 80 or ₉₀?

742. Three days is what fraction of a week?

890. Subtract seven-hundredths from three-tenths.

939. Darlene made a budget for her wedding. She planned on spending one-half on her dress, one-third on food, and one-sixth on flowers. How much did she have left over to spend on a wedding present for Joe?

from
B R I D A L   G O W N S
magazine

from
B R I D A L   F E A S T S
magazine

from
F L O W E R S
magazine

Chapter Seventeen
Improper Fractions

First part: Problems from this chapter

337. Change $\dfrac{44}{7}$ into a mixed number.

366. LCM stands for _____?_____.
     LCD stands for _____?_____.

442. After Joe caught his first fish, he celebrated by drinking $\dfrac{4}{5}$ of a cup of Sluice.

    After his second fish, he drank $\dfrac{2}{3}$ cup of Sluice.

    After his third fish, he drank $\dfrac{1}{2}$ cup Sluice.

    In all that celebration how much Sluice did he drink? (Do not leave your answer as an improper fraction.)

459. Sluice is almost all sugar.

    The formula for making Sluice is: Take a pile of sugar and dampen it with a drop or two of water. (For extra flavor, use turtle spit instead.)

    When Joe drank almost two cups of Sluice, his body went into hyperglycemia. (Translation: *hyper* = too much, *glycos* = sugar.)

    When kids at birthday parties have too much cake and candy, they sometimes go a little nuts. They run around like crazy. They scream a lot, and they often end up crying. Moms sometimes call this a "sugar high."

    Normal adults who haven't eaten anything in several hours have blood sugar levels of about 4 or 5 mmol/l. (mmol/l = millimoles per liter, which will be explained in chemistry) People who are consistently between 6 and 7 mmol/l are considered hyperglycemic by the American Diabetes Association. Chronically over 7 mmol/l and you will often be considered diabetic.

    Hyperglycemia over long periods of time can bring on *serious* problems: kidney damage, eye damage (to the retina), and heart damage.

(continued on next page)

You know Joe's eating habits (jelly beans and Sluice). There are six chances in seven that he's going to have serious health problems because of his diet. Express six chances in seven as a fraction.

530. Darlene keeps encouraging Joe to propose marriage to her. She gives him lots of hints, such as leaving bridal magazines scattered around her apartment and talking about wonderful places to have a honeymoon and how many children they might have.

She estimates that there is two chances in ten that he will propose to her before they graduate from college. Express this as a fraction.

565. (continuing the previous problem) What are the chances that Joe will not propose before graduation?

626. Darlene explains to Joe that if they were married, she could cook all his favorite foods for him every day.

Joe told her that his favorite Wednesday dish is Frijoles & Beans:

$\frac{3}{4}$ cup vanilla jelly beans

$\frac{3}{4}$ cup cherry jelly beans

$\frac{3}{4}$ cup orange jelly beans

Place in bowl and stir well. Serve cold.

Darlene said that she would be happy to make that every Wednesday of their married life. How many cups would this recipe make?

Second part: the 𝕸ixed 𝕭ag: a variety of problems from this chapter and previous chapters

220. What is the least common denominator for fractions whose denominators are 12 and 16?

346. Express 230 minutes in hours and minutes.

368. Express 230 minutes in hours.

434. Change $\frac{39}{6}$ into a mixed number.

520. In the PieOne kitchen Fred had 6 pounds of hamburger. He was supposed to spread that evenly on 8 pizzas. How much would each pizza receive?

649. Fred had a pan that was 14" × 30" and he wanted to make the largest round pizza to fit in that pan. What will be the diameter of that pizza?

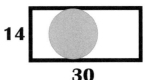

667. (continuing the previous problem) What will be the radius of that pizza?

693. There are 600 seats in the PieOne restaurant. If 400 of them are occupied, what *fraction* of the seats are empty?

738. If five-eighths of the customers at PieOne are math majors, what fraction of the customers are not math majors?

802. $932 \times 31 \times 55819 \times 0 = ?$

876. When Joe goes out fishing, there is three-fourths of a chance that he will injure himself. (That's three chances out of four.) He sometimes cuts himself. Sometimes he falls overboard. Sometimes he gets sunburned. Sometimes he hits his head with an oar.

   One spring he went fishing for 80 days. How many days during that spring did he injure himself?
   (Hint: This is the same as asking $\frac{3}{4} = \frac{?}{80}$)

Chapter Eighteen
Lines of Symmetry

First part: Problems from this chapter

Here's another way to look at symmetry.

Suppose you take a piece of paper and draw some shape using a very wet pen.

Then you fold the paper.

The resulting picture
has a line of symmetry (along the fold).

===

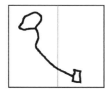

If you draw this with a wet pen
and fold the paper,

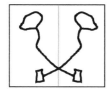

then you get a picture
with a line of symmetry
along the fold.

(continued on next page)

382. Now it's your turn to draw. If you start with this picture and you fold it, what will you get?

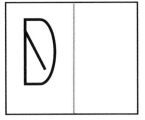

Sometimes you are given a picture and you are asked whether it has a line of symmetry.

One way to see if it has a line of symmetry is to try to fold the wet drawing. If you can fold it and *not* make any new lines, then it has a line of symmetry along the fold.

455. Does this picture have a line of symmetry along the fold?

500.

This doesn't have symmetry along a vertical $\updownarrow$ fold.
What if we fold it diagonally?

665.

Does this have a line of symmetry?

Second part: the 𝔐ixed 𝔅ag: a variety of problems from this chapter and previous chapters

113. Change 755 minutes into hours and minutes.
    To change minutes into hours you divide by 60.

245. Which is smaller: $\dfrac{13}{20}$ or $\dfrac{19}{30}$?

380. Change $\dfrac{604}{7}$ into a mixed number.

433. Does this have a line of symmetry?
(This is the schematic of a bi-polar transistor.)

(*schematic* = diagram of an electrical or
mechanical system)

488. Express 324 seconds in minutes and seconds.

527. Express 324 seconds in minutes.

569. If Joe spent $\dfrac{31}{33}$ of his day thinking about fishing, what fraction of his day was left to think about other things?

635. Darlene once asked Joe, "How often each day do you think about me?"
    She offered him the choice of any natural number. The natural numbers are sometimes written as ℕ.
    ℕ = {1, 2, 3, 4, 5, 6, . . . }.
    Joe couldn't answer. He couldn't think of a natural number that was true.
    He wanted to pick a number out of the whole numbers. Why?

662. Darlene did everything she could think of to attract Joe's attention. She would often go with him on his fishing boat, even though she hated fishing. She would cook him his favorite foods. She often helped him with his fractions homework. She wore fancy nail polish. She dreamed of grabbing him by his two ears and shouting, "Joe, look at me!"
    She read in one of her bridal magazines an article entitled "Fifteen Ways to Get Him to Notice You." Is 15 an ordinal number?

Chapter Nineteen
Division by Zero

First part: Problems from this chapter

384. Darlene saw a sale on dresses. "All dresses $24!!!!!" She also noticed: "No sales tax if you pay cash!!!!!"

     Darlene borrowed $384 from her mom and rushed to the store. How many dresses could she buy?

436. When she got to the store, she was delighted. The dresses were all marked $12 (instead of $24). How many dresses could she buy at that price?

466. If the dresses were $8, she could buy $\frac{384}{8}$ = 48 dresses.

If the dresses were $6, she could buy $\frac{384}{6}$ = 64 dresses.

If the dresses were $2, she could buy $\frac{384}{2}$ = 192 dresses.

If the dresses were free, she could buy $\frac{384}{0}$ How many is this?

477. There is a reason Coalback Clothing could offer cheap prices. When Darlene got home with 1,488 dresses, she noticed that one-third of them had broken zippers. How many had broken zippers?

498. Six of the 1,488 dresses that Darlene bought were wedding dresses. Darlene told herself, "You can never have too many wedding dresses."

     Her mom shook her head and said, "What are you going to do with six wedding dresses? You only get married once."

     Darlene explained to her mom that she read in a bridal magazine about this movie star that changed her dress five times during the ceremony.

     What fraction of the dresses that Darlene bought were wedding dresses?

Second part: the 𝔐ixed 𝔅ag: a variety of problems from this chapter and previous chapters

397. Darlene's mom told Darlene, "All you seem to think about is your wedding day. What about the 50 years of married life that follow that one day?"

Darlene said, "But the wedding day is my day!"

One day is what fraction of 50 years? (Assume 365 days = 1 year.)

508. A barrel of oil is 42 gallons. One gallon is 4 quarts. How many quarts are in a barrel?

522. (continuing the previous problem) Darlene was going to order a barrel of salad oil for her wedding reception. Fill in this chart:

salad oil available	each guest uses	number of servings
168 quarts	4 quarts	$\frac{168}{4} = 42$
168 quarts	2 quarts	?
168 quarts	1 quarts	?
168 quarts	0 quarts	?

571. Darlene found salad oil that she was sure no one would like. Until what year was this salad oil good?

She wanted salad dressing that was really stale so that no one would want to use it.

Salad Oil

good till MCMXL

608. Darlene read about the newest craze for wedding reception food: personalized marshmallows. Which is larger?

$\frac{2}{3}$ oz.

$\frac{7}{10}$ oz.

Chapter Twenty

Subtracting Fractions

First part: Problems from this chapter

385. Jelly beans don't rot. Bacteria are smarter than Joe. They won't eat jelly beans.

     In contrast, bacteria love real food. Real food goes in the refrigerator so that it stays cold enough that bacteria lose their appetite.

     Joe went to the grocery store and bought 50 pounds of jelly beans and $\frac{5}{6}$ lb. of cheese. He took the jelly beans into his apartment, but left the cheese in the car for a couple of days.

     Three-fourths of a pound of that cheese "went bad." Joe cut the bad cheese off of the $\frac{5}{6}$ pound. How much was left?

438. Joe wasn't sure what to do with the $\frac{3}{4}$ of a pound of bad cheese. He put $\frac{3}{8}$ lb. of it into his scrapbook. The rest he fed to his fish. How much did he feed to his fish?

463. The fish were smart enough not to eat the rotten cheese, but they were trapped in the bad water.

     The tank had $\frac{4}{5}$ of a gallon of water in it. All the fish died.

Joe poured $\frac{3}{4}$ of a gallon of water out of the tank into the dumpster in back of the apartment house. How much water was left in the tank?

479. When the garbage truck came to empty the dumpster, $\frac{5}{16}$ of a gallon

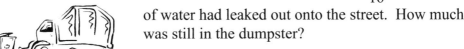

of water had leaked out onto the street. How much was still in the dumpster?

Second part: the 𝔐ixed 𝔅ag: a variety of problems from this chapter and previous chapters

399. $\dfrac{11}{15} - \dfrac{2}{9} = ?$

447. What is the smallest whole number?

492. Joe was unhappy that the fish in his aquarium died. (But he was happy when he went fishing and killed fish.)

He needed to blow his nose and wipe his eyes. He unrolled 280 inches of toilet paper. "That will certainly do the job," he told himself. How many feet and inches is that?

510. How many feet is 280"?

524. In Roman numerals, the letter X can only go in front of _?_ or _?_ .

533. Darlene had always told Joe not to waste things. Joe took the $23\frac{1}{3}$ feet of wet toilet paper and wrapped his dead aquarium fish in it.

He knew that the dead fish wouldn't mind being wrapped in something that was wet. "After all," he thought, "they used to live in water."

He said goodbye and threw it toward the waste basket.
The waste basket was across the room.
He missed.
It hit the wall.
It stuck.
It was 4 feet, 3 inches from the floor.

Convert that to inches.

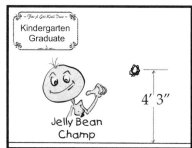

Joe's wall

601. Joe was most proud of his Kindergarten graduation certificate. It took him three years to earn it. Is 3 a cardinal number?

Chapter Twenty-one
Circumference

First part: Problems from this chapter

386. $\frac{2}{3} \times \frac{7}{8} = ?$

473. The word *of* between two numbers often mean multiply.
What is three-fifths of two-thirds?

512. Fred has always liked to jog. One of
his favorite jogging places on the
KITTENS campus is called Tree Circle.
   The diameter of that circle is
6 miles. One trip around that circle was a
good way to start Fred's exercise day.

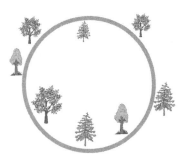

The distance around a circle is called the
circumference (sir-COME-fur-ence)

   A strange fact of nature is: **The circumference
of a circle is always a little more than three times its diameter.** It doesn't
matter if the circle is → ○ or is miles across.
   If you multiply the diameter of a circle by 3, you get a good idea
what the circumference is.
   Roughly, how far would Fred jog if he went once around Tree
Circle?

535. If the radius of a circle is 5 meters, what is its approximate
circumference?

Second part: the 𝔐ixed 𝔅ag: a variety of problems from this chapter and previous chapters

260. Fred could go 69 mph riding on his train. How far could he go in 7 hours?

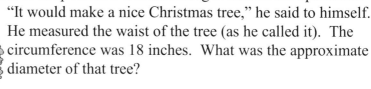

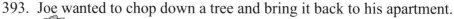

393. Joe wanted to chop down a tree and bring it back to his apartment. "It would make a nice Christmas tree," he said to himself. He measured the waist of the tree (as he called it). The circumference was 18 inches. What was the approximate diameter of that tree?

Joe's tape measure

695. If Joe chopped down a tree from Tree Circle on the KITTENS University campus, he would have done something that is wrong, dumb, and illegal.

The fine for chopping down campus trees is $500. Joe had saved up $650 in his checking account to buy jelly beans.

$500 is what fraction of $650?

714. When Joe is attending one of Fred's 60-minute lectures, he spends three-tenths of the time doodling on his binder paper. How many minutes is that?

747. $\frac{1}{6} + \frac{1}{8}$ = ?

796. What is the least common multiple (LCM) of 5, 25, and 100?

822. $\frac{1}{5} \times \frac{3}{8} \times \frac{13}{33} \times \frac{0}{15}$ = ?

Chapter Twenty-two
Multiplying Mixed Numbers

First part: Problems from this chapter

387. Change $6\frac{2}{3}$ into an improper fraction.

537. The diameter of Tree Circle is 6 miles. What is the approximate circumference if we multiply by $3\frac{1}{7}$?

574. $4\frac{1}{4} \times 4\frac{1}{4} = ?$

612. To find the area of a rectangle you multiply length times width.

w

$A = \ell w$

ℓ

    If my living room is $8\frac{1}{2}$ feet wide and $12\frac{3}{4}$ feet long, how many square feet of carpet will I need?

642. Change into improper fractions: $5\frac{2}{5}$ $10\frac{3}{4}$ $2\frac{1}{16}$

687. Change $\frac{706}{9}$ into a mixed number.

Second part: the 𝔐ixed 𝔅ag: a variety of problems from this chapter and previous chapters

127. Can you think of a number—let's call it y—so that 2y = 7?

347. Change $\frac{638}{8}$ into a mixed number.

388. Which is smaller: $\frac{2}{7}$ or $\frac{3}{8}$?

448. Does this have a line of symmetry?

467. Joe dreamed about having a field filled with jelly beans.

$7\frac{1}{6}$

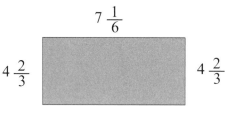

$4\frac{2}{3}$ $4\frac{2}{3}$

$7\frac{1}{6}$

It was a rectangle that measured $4\frac{2}{3}$ by $7\frac{1}{6}$ miles. It was a big field. How many square miles was it?

481. (continuing previous problem) A jelly bean bear walked around the outside of Joe's jelly bean field. He was looking for a way to get in. Joe had built a big fence to keep out jelly bean bears.

He walked all the way around the outside. How far did he walk?

Another way to ask this question: What is the *perimeter* of that rectangle? (pronounced per-RIM-eh-ter)

Chapter Twenty-three
Commutative Law

First part: Problems from this chapter

493. Joe was reading Prof. Eldwood's book *The Modern Way to Eat Jelly Beans*, 1842. Joe wanted to do it right.

  The book said that there are two steps. Joe wrote down in his notebook: Two steps.

  The book said that you first stick the jelly beans in your mouth. Then the second step is to chew them.

  Are these two steps commutative?

516. It was Wednesday and Joe was going out fishing in his boat. Darlene asked to come along. She put 4 bottles of nail polish in her purse. Then she decided that might not be enough and put in 3 more bottles. "You can never have too much nail polish," she told herself.

  If she had first put 3 bottles in her purse and then put in 4 more bottles, she would have the same result.

  This illustrates which of the following?

    A) Nail polish is necessary on fishing trips.
    B) Addition is commutative.
    C) Multiplication is commutative.
    D) Darlene can't count.

542. In the boat Darlene painted her toenails with Wow-Pink™ polish. Joe complained about the smell. She didn't like the way her toenails looked, so she painted them with Pucker-Purple™ polish. Joe complained again about the smell. Darlene thought Joe's complaints were silly since the bottom of his boat was filled with rotting fish that he had caught on previous fishing trips.

  Is putting on pink polish followed by purple polish commutative?

605. Darlene wanted to look her best for her man. She first brushed her hair for 20 minutes and then put on Cyanotic-Blue™ lipstick. (Cyanotic is in your dictionary under cyanosis.) Are brushing hair and putting on lipstick commutative?

Second part: the 𝔐ixed 𝔅ag: a variety of problems from this chapter and previous chapters

135. I'm thinking of a number—call it y—so that 2y = 9. What is that number?   2y means "two times y."

580. 68 × 69

670. The United States Postal Service asked Joe to design a new stamp.

This is what Joe came up with:

The USPS rejected Joe's submission for several obvious reasons.

Joe's stamp was $6 \frac{1}{8}$ inches wide and $7 \frac{3}{4}$ inches long. (The USPS didn't like stamps that wouldn't fit on envelopes.)
What was the area of Joe's stamp?   A = 𝓁𝔀 for rectangles

704. How many lines of symmetry does a square have? (Hint: The answer is not two.)

750. $\frac{8}{15} - \frac{2}{15} = ?$

798. After about four hours of fishing and eating bags of jelly beans, Joe gets tired of swallowing jelly beans. (I know this is hard to believe, but even Joe can get full of jelly beans.)
Joe had run out of worms to put on his fishing hooks, so he invented Joe's Special Jelly Bean Worms.™
First, he put 7 licorice (black) jelly beans in his mouth and chewed them up into a paste.
Then he squirted out (like toothpaste tube) a black worm. Darlene thought this was gross, but she didn't complain. How many jelly beans would it take to make 500 worms?

Chapter Twenty-four
Adding Mixed Numbers

First part: Problems from this chapter

When you **multiply** mixed numbers, you have to first change them into improper fractions.

$$5\frac{2}{3} \times 3\frac{1}{2} = \frac{17}{3} \times \frac{7}{2} = \frac{119}{6} = 6\overline{)119}^{\,19\,R\,5} = 19\frac{5}{6}$$

When you **add** mixed numbers, you leave them as mixed numbers.

$$5\frac{2}{3} + 3\frac{1}{2}$$

$$
\begin{aligned}
5\frac{2}{3} &= 5\frac{4}{6}\\
3\frac{1}{2} &= 3\frac{3}{6}\\
\hline
8\frac{7}{6} &= 8 + 1\frac{1}{6} = 9\frac{1}{6}
\end{aligned}
$$

544. Darlene wanted to make a new color nail polish. She combined $2\frac{3}{4}$ ounces of blue polish with $3\frac{7}{8}$ ounces of brown polish. The result was a gray muddy polish that she called "sunset in the swamp." Instead of using it as nail polish, she used it to paste stickers in her sticker album. How many ounces of sunset in the swamp had she created?

546. $4\frac{537}{600} \times 0 = ?$

555. $4\frac{539}{600} + 0 = ?$

614. Joe dreamed about a new jelly bean field that had five sides. It had a big fence to keep out jelly bean bears.

  The bear walked around the outside looking for a way to get in. What is the perimeter (the distance around) Joe's jelly bean field?

  The distances are all measured in miles.

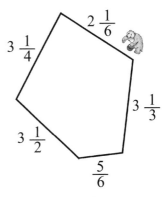

Second part: the 𝔐ixed 𝔅ag: a variety of problems from this chapter and previous chapters

177. I'm thinking of a number—call it x—such that x + 3 = 8¼. What is that number?

232. What is the least common denominator for fractions whose denominators are 3, 4, 5, and 6?

348. At the wedding reception Darlene imagined that Joe would help out in the kitchen. She knew this would have two advantages: ① It would save money, and ② it would keep him out of the way. She wanted everyone at the wedding to pay attention to her.

   Joe had 18 bottles of Sluice and he was assigned to pour that evenly into 30 glasses. How much should go into each glass?

673. Darlene read an article in one of her bridal magazines: "The Perfect Bridal Tiara." She asked her mother what a tiara was. (pronounced tea-AIR-eh or tea-ARE-eh) Her mom said that it was a jeweled coronet worn by women.

   Darlene asked her what a coronet was. Her mom told her that a coronet was a small crown.

   "Yes!" thought Darlene. "I need one of those."

   She ordered one on the Internet and asked for extra jewels. Her final selection had $2\frac{7}{8}$ pounds of diamonds, $3\frac{2}{3}$ pounds of sapphires, $\frac{5}{6}$ pounds of emeralds, and $2\frac{3}{4}$ pounds of rhinestones.

   How much did all of these jewels weigh?

697. Sapphires are often blue—but not always. When Darlene looked at the $3\frac{2}{3}$ pounds of sapphires on her tiara, she noticed that $\frac{1}{2}$ pound of them were not blue. She dug those non-blue gems out of her tiara. Now all of the sapphires in her crown were blue. This was important to her since she was going to have her hair dyed blue for the wedding.

   How many pounds of sapphires were left in her crown?

Chapter Twenty-five
Canceling

First part: Problems from this chapter

You can cancel only when you are **multiplying** fractions.

611. $\frac{4}{15} \times \frac{5}{8} = ?$

644. $4\frac{1}{6} \times \frac{1}{15} = ?$

677. Darlene noticed that two-fifths of the $2\frac{7}{8}$ pounds of diamonds in her tiara were highly flawed. She said that they looked like they had bugs in them.

     How many pounds of flawed diamonds did she have?

706. Darlene telephoned the Internet company that had sold her the tiara and the extra jewels. She said that a lot of her diamonds had big bugs in them.

     The salesman said, "That is what you should expect if you are buying diamonds *by the pound*."

     Darlene said that she had paid $200 for the diamonds and asked, "How much more would it have cost if I had ordered just flawless diamonds instead?"

     He said, "It would cost four and a half times as much."

     How much would that be?

753. Have fun canceling! $\frac{5}{6} \times \frac{2}{15} \times \frac{9}{13}$

825. Joe did this problem right $\frac{3}{4} \times \frac{5}{6} = \frac{\overset{1}{3}}{4} \times \frac{5}{\underset{2}{6}} = \frac{5}{8}$

     Then he did $\frac{7}{9} + \frac{11}{14} = \frac{\overset{1}{7}}{9} + \frac{11}{\underset{2}{14}} = \frac{11}{18}$

Did he make a mistake?

Second part: the 𝔐ixed 𝔅ag: a variety of problems from this chapter and previous chapters

383. If Darlene spent $\frac{3}{8}$ of her money on clothes and nail polish, what fraction did she have left to spend on other things (such as rent, food, and books)?

514. Which of these is smaller: $\frac{5}{12}$ or $\frac{2}{5}$?

702. Joe was going to be assigned to work in the kitchen during the wedding reception. The kitchen floor was $10\frac{1}{4}$ feet by $16\frac{1}{2}$ feet. What was its area?

745. (continuing the previous problem) Joe figured that the first thing he should do is wax the kitchen floor. He estimated that it would take 8 seconds to do each square foot. How long would it take for him to do the whole floor?

880. The kitchen floor was $10\frac{1}{4}$ feet by $16\frac{1}{2}$ feet. A mouse ran around the perimeter of that floor so that he wouldn't get his feet full of wax. How far did he go?

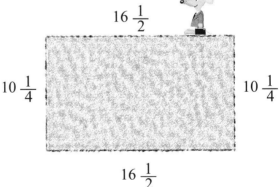

$16\frac{1}{2}$

$10\frac{1}{4}$ $10\frac{1}{4}$

$16\frac{1}{2}$

942. (Tricky question) When Joe saw the mouse, he felt sorry for him. He decided to buy the mouse some shoes so that he wouldn't get wax on his feet. On the Internet he found SUPER SOFT MOUSE SHOES—MADE FROM CAT FUR. ONLY $4 each.

Joe sent in $8. Why was this a mistake?

Chapter Twenty-six
Opposites

First part: Problems from this chapter

When you do the opposite you want to end up where you began.
If you **double something**, the opposite rule is to **take half of it** (or **divide by 2**). If I double 5, I get 10. If I take half of 10, I get 5.

615. What is the opposite rule for **taking half of something**?

636. What is the opposite rule for **divide by six**?

656. If I write with a pencil on paper, the opposite is to erase it.
If I write with a ballpoint pen on paper, there is no opposite action. There is no way (that I know of) to undo that action and get back to the original paper that has no writing on it.
    Which of these have opposite actions?
    A) Putting on a hat.
    B) Shutting your eyes.
    C) Eating a slice of pizza.
    D) Opening a door.
    E) Adding 829 to a number.
    F) Multiplying by zero.

If you do two things, one after another, then the opposite action is to do the opposite of those things *in reverse order*. For example, if you put on your shoes and then walk from home to the library, the opposite action is to first walk home from the library and then take off your shoes.
    It is not take off your shoes and then walk home! Ouch.

707. What is the opposite to **add 3 and then multiply by 10**?

Second part: the 𝔐ixed 𝔅ag: a variety of problems from this chapter and previous chapters

205. Think of a number. Call it x. Is it ever possible that 0x = 4?
   0x means "zero times x."

617. In Darlene's dreams of marrying Joe, she had many things to worry about.
   Worry #1: What if Joe forgets about the wedding date and goes out fishing instead?
   Solution: I will hire some guy to stay with Joe for the 24 hours before the wedding to make sure he remembers to get to the wedding. A man from Groom-Guard™ costs $17/hour. How much will it cost Darlene for this service?

641. Darlene's Worry #2: What if Joe brings his boat to the wedding?
   Solution: We will put the boat outside and tie a rope to the boat and hand the other end of the rope to Joe. Then he can hold onto the rope during the ceremony. The rope will be 450 inches long.
   How long is 450" in feet and inches?

671. How long is 450" in feet?

682. Darlene's Worry #3: What if Joe won't let go of the rope and his boat during the honeymoon?
   Solution: We have the honeymoon in his boat. I always dreamed of going to Hawaii on my honeymoon. If it's 3000 miles away, how long will it take us if we go 27 miles per day in his boat?

712. Darlene's Worry #4: Once I get married, I can get rid of my collection of bridal magazines, my dieting books, my high-heel shoes. In other words, I can get comfortable. I have $273 \frac{3}{8}$ pounds of stuff I can toss in the garbage. If everything I own weighs $328 \frac{3}{4}$ pounds, how much will I have left after the wedding?

Chapter Twenty-seven
Area of a Rectangle

First part: Problems from this chapter

The area of a rectangle is equal to length times width. In algebra we write this as A = ℓw.

621. Joe was in the habit of trying to study while he was fishing on his boat. This didn't work because he didn't have a place to put down a piece of paper and write on it. Darlene gave Joe a desk so that he could do his school work. The top of his desk was black. (It was a rectangle that measured 2 $\frac{1}{2}$ feet by 3 $\frac{1}{3}$ feet.) What was the area of this desktop?

684. (continuing the previous problem) Joe decided to paint his desktop orange, which was his favorite color. The man at the paint store told Joe that it would cost 5 $\frac{1}{5}$ ¢ to paint each square foot. How much would it cost to paint his desktop?

699. One square foot measures 12 inches by 12 inches. What is the area of a square foot in square inches?

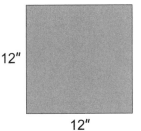

12"

12"

717. Joe's desktop is 8 $\frac{1}{3}$ square feet. How many square inches is that?

Second part: the Ⓜ️ixed Ⓑ️ag: a variety of problems from this chapter and previous chapters

437. Every Sunday Joe would put on seven shirts. He was a very messy eater. By the end of the day, his outside shirt would be splattered with ketchup, Sluice, and jelly bean drool. (Joe was the only one who could dirty a shirt while eating jelly beans.)

Each evening Joe would take off one shirt. On Saturday night he would remove his seventh shirt. That reminded him to take a bath.

Is *seventh* a cardinal number?

623. Each of Joe's shirts had $12 \frac{3}{4}$ grams of jelly bean drool on it.

(A gram is about the weight of a raisin.) What was the weight of the jelly bean drool on all seven shirts?

708. Each shirt had $3 \frac{1}{2}$ grams of ketchup, $2 \frac{1}{8}$ grams of Sluice, and $12 \frac{3}{4}$ grams of jelly bean drool on it.
What was the weight of all that mess on each shirt?

755. Joe liked to play in the bathtub. As an experiment he dropped a spoonful of ketchup into the water. It spread out into a pretty red circle.

The diameter of that circle was $8 \frac{1}{4}$ inches. What was the circumference of that circle. (For this problem we'll say that the circumference is equal to $3 \frac{1}{7}$ times the diameter.)

792. When Joe got out of the bathtub, his skin was more pink than normal. Why?

823. Divide MMDCXIX by XXVII and express your answer in Roman numerals.

Chapter Twenty-eight
Unit Analysis

First part: Problems from this chapter

Conversion factors. You want to convert 17 weeks into days.
Step 1: You know that 1 week = 7 days.
Step 2: The conversion factor will be either $\frac{1 \text{ week}}{7 \text{ days}}$ or $\frac{7 \text{ days}}{1 \text{ week}}$

This conversion factor is always equal to one because the top and bottom of the fraction are equal to each other. (See step 1.)

Step 3: You are given the 17 weeks. That means $\frac{17 \text{ weeks}}{1}$

Step 4: You pick the conversion factor (from step 2) so that the units cancel. $\frac{17 \text{ weeks}}{1} \times \frac{7 \text{ days}}{1 \text{ week}} = 119 \text{ days}$

624. Convert 8 years into months using a conversion factor.

721. When Darlene is on the boat while Joe is fishing, he has her clean the fish that he's caught. She can clean 5 fish in 8 minutes. Using a conversion factor find out how long it would take her to clean 30 fish.

788. She likes to read bridal magazines while she cleans Joe's fish. Many of the articles tell her that she should do whatever it takes to make Joe think that she is happy doing this job for him.

She reads 4 magazine pages for every 7 fish she cleans. How many pages will she read while cleaning 30 fish? Use a conversion factor.

868. Joe could never figure out why Darlene was so happy to clean the fish he caught. (He had never read the articles in the bridal magazines.) In order to make Darlene happier, he invented new system of catching fish. For every 5 fish he caught under the old system, he could catch 8 under the new system. If he caught 20 under the old system, he many could he catch under the new system. Use a conversion factor.

Second part: the 𝕸ixed 𝕭ag: a variety of problems from this chapter and previous chapters

417. How many whole numbers are less than 3?

441. Twenty minutes is what fraction of an hour?

639. To find the square of a number you multiply the number by itself. The square of 7 is 49.

Finding the square root of a number is the opposite operation. The square root of 49 is 7.

What is the square root of 25?

757. Which of these is easier to do?

A) $\dfrac{7}{9} + \dfrac{1}{8}$

B) $\dfrac{7}{9} \times \dfrac{1}{8}$

804. Fifty feet of fishing line cost $3. Using a conversion factor, find out how much 75 feet would cost.

824. Are the operations of *square a number* and *add 3* commutative?

872. Change $10\,\dfrac{3}{4}$ into an improper fraction.

920. Write three millionths as a fraction.

940. Darlene went with Joe on one of his fishing trips. She brought along  some of her bridal magazines. While she was reading all those magazines, she was hoping that Joe would someday get the hint about their getting married.

On their forty-second fishing trip Joe finally asked Darlene why she was reading all those bridal magazines. Darlene knew this was her opportunity to bring up the subject of marriage.

Darlene said, "I read those bridal magazines because I hope, some day, to become a bride. Isn't that obvious?"

Joe held up a copy of the one magazine he subscribes to—AMERICAN JELLY BEAN.

Now you finish the story. What did Joe say to Darlene?

Chapter Twenty-nine
Subtracting Mixed Numbers

First part: Problems from this chapter

668. Joe had chopped down a tree from Tree Circle. The tree was 12 feet tall. When he dragged it back to his apartment, Darlene looked at it and said, "This is too tall for your apartment." The ceiling in Joe's apartment is $8\frac{1}{3}$ feet tall. How much will Joe have to shorten his tree?

760. $8\frac{1}{3} - 4\frac{2}{3}$

784. In Joe's favorite magazine, AMERICAN JELLY BEAN, there was an article entitled "Jelly Bean Storage Buildings." The article pointed out that one of the most important things is not to get your jelly beans wet. "Build your storage building $12\frac{3}{4}$ feet off the ground."

Suppose the flood waters are $2\frac{7}{8}$ feet deep. How much higher could they rise before they reach the bottom of the building?

806. A jelly bean storage building can hold 2 tons of jelly beans. Currently, Joe has one-sixteenth of a ton of jelly beans. How much more jelly beans would Joe need in order to fill that building?

828. One sixteenth of a ton is how many pounds? (one ton = 2,000 pounds)

Second part: the 𝔐ixed 𝔅ag: a variety of problems from this chapter and previous chapters

700. Which has the greatest number of Calories?
      A) Sixteen popsicles, each with 95 Calories
      B) Two ice cream sodas, each with 762 Calories
      C) Three small cherry pies, each with 513 Calories

705. If 3,500 Calories translates into one pound of fat on your tummy, what would 4,000 Calories equal in terms of fat?   (Use a conversion factor.)

759. What is the square of $5\frac{1}{3}$?

810. What is the square root of 64?

874. Each of Joe's shirts had $12\frac{3}{4}$ grams of jelly bean drool on it. A gram of jelly bean drool is equal to $3\frac{4}{51}$ Calories. If the ants ate the jelly bean drool off of one of his shirts, how many Calories would they receive? (Use a conversion factor.)

903. If Joe's shirt weighed $500\frac{1}{6}$ grams with the jelly bean drool on it, how much would it weigh after the ants removed the $12\frac{3}{4}$ grams of jelly bean drool?

945. What is the smallest cardinal number?

Chapter Thirty
Division by a Fraction

First part: Problems from this chapter

761. $\frac{4}{5} \div \frac{8}{9} = ?$

812. Suppose there existed 3¢ coins. If you wanted to spend 12¢, you would use 4 coins. $12 \div 3$ tells you how many 3's there are in 12.

In the same way, Joe had $2\frac{1}{2}$ ounce packages of worms for fishing.

How many of those packages would he need if he wanted $17\frac{1}{2}$ ounces of worms?

830. Darlene's most expensive nail polish is CURIE'S GLOW-IN-THE-LIGHT NAIL POLISH.™ There are some nail polishes that glow in the dark, but CURIE'S is different. It glows even in the daylight. (It's radioactive.) It costs $5 for a $\frac{1}{6}$ ounce bottle.

Darlene needs 4 ounces. (She is doing both finger and toe nails and is putting in several coats.) How many bottles does she need?

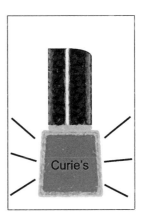

878. Darlene was going to use bottles of CURIE'S GLOW-IN-THE-LIGHT NAIL POLISH™ to light up her room at night. She imagined that they would be better than having a night light because she wouldn't have to turn them on or off each night. They would just glow. Each bottle would put out $3\frac{3}{4}$ lumens of light. (A lumen is a measure of brightness. If you look on a light bulb package, you may see the brightness listed.)

WATTS	
	Lasts 2400 Hours
Light Output 615 Lumens	To save energy costs, find the bulbs with the light output you need,
Energy Used 60 Watts	then choose the one with the lowest watts. Additional savings can
Life 2466 Hours	be had by choosing a longer life bulb.

Now you know what a lumen is.

How many bottles will Darlene need to get 615 lumens of light?

Second part: the 𝔐ixed 𝔅ag: a variety of problems from this chapter and previous chapters

456. What is four-fifths of $3\frac{3}{4}$?

758. In one of the bridal magazines was an article entitled, "Get Him to Notice You!" Darlene thought that was a good idea. She headed to Pat—her favorite hairdresser—and asked him if he would paint her hair with CURIE'S GLOW-IN-THE-LIGHT NAIL POLISH.™

He told her that her hair would be hard as a rock if he did that. Darlene said, "That will be okay. It will save on hair spray costs."

Pat said, "It will cost you $\frac{4}{11}$ ¢ per hair to do that. That nail polish is super expensive."

Darlene said, "Start painting."

When Pat was done, the bill was $40 (which is 4,000¢).

How many hairs are on Darlene's head?

762. Darlene got her hair painted. The next time she saw Joe, she asked him, "Well, what do you think?"

"About what?" Joe asked.

Darlene winced and said, "About my hair."

Joe scratched his uncombed hair. "I have an idea. We could go fishing together in my boat tonight."

Darlene was hoping Joe was having a romantic thought. Her hopes were dashed when he said, "Your head is glowing. I wouldn't need to bring a flashlight."

Darlene had spent $40. Her total budget for her hair for the whole year was $200. What fraction of her hair budget was wasted on getting her hair painted?

813. She went back to her hairdresser and asked him to remove the CURIE'S GLOW-IN-THE-LIGHT NAIL POLISH from her hair. Pat had to wear sunglasses because of the brightness of Darlene's head. Using a hammer and nail polish remover, he was able to clean 100 hairs in $2\frac{1}{2}$ minutes. At that rate, how

long will it take Pat to clean up the 11,000 hairs on Darlene's head? (Use a conversion factor.)

882. (continuing the previous problem) How many hours and minutes will it take Pat?

Marie Curie

I invented the **Curie's Glow-in-the-Light Nail Polish**, but I did not invent Marie Curie. She is very real.

✶ Marie Curie was the first woman to win a Nobel prize.
✶ She was the first person to ever win two Nobel prizes.
✶ She was the only woman to win Nobel prizes in two fields.
✶ She was the only person to win Nobel prizes in two sciences.

In July 1898 she and her husband Pierre announced the discovery of the chemical element polonium. Since they had discovered it, they were allowed to name it. Polonium was named after Poland, the country Marie was born in.

Five months later they announced the discovery of another chemical element, radium.

These two elements are radioactive, but no one before them had ever called them radioactive. That's because they invented the word *radioactivity*.

She used to store test tubes containing radioactive material in her desk drawer. Those test tubes glowed faintly in the dark. She sometimes carried those test tubes in her pocket. No one at that time knew that long-term exposure to heavy radioactivity had health risks.

With decades of exposure she developed aplastic anemia and died. Twenty-eight years before that, Pierre died when he was hit by a horse-drawn vehicle.

Pierre and Marie

Chapter Thirty-one
Geometry

First part: Problems from this chapter

780. Is it possible to draw a triangle with two right angles?

789. A pentagon is a figure with five sides. How many vertices does it have? (*Vertices* is the plural of *vertex*. In geometry a corner of a figure is called a vertex.)

831. In geometry a four-sided figure is called a quadrilateral.
   In geometry these are parallel.
If you make these parallel lines longer,
they will never touch each other.

   If I have a quadrilateral in which the opposite sides are parallel, must it be a rectangle?

885. If I have a quadrilateral in which all the vertices are right angles, must it be a rectangle?

right angle

891. (harder question) A pentagon has five sides and five vertices. Is it possible for a pentagon to have four right angles?

926. Is it possible for a pentagon to have three right angles?

947. A *regular* hexagon is a six-sided figure with all the sides and all the angles equal.
   A *regular* pentagon is a five-sided figure with all the sides and all the angles equal.

   What do you call a regular quadrilateral?

Second part: the 𝔐ixed 𝔅ag: a variety of problems from this chapter and previous chapters

490. Stanthony's PieOne Pizza offers a 36-pound special wedding pizza. Darlene was thinking of offering a quarter-pound to each of her guests at the wedding reception. How many people would this serve?

That's the same as asking how many $\frac{1}{4}$'s are there in 36.

645. In chemistry we know that one mole of carbon weighs 12 grams. How many moles are in 30 grams? (Use a conversion factor.)

834. Darlene gave Joe a comb. Even though the articles in all the bridal magazines told her to never criticize anything about his appearance, she did it anyway.

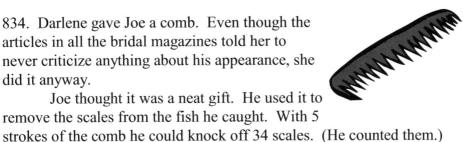

Joe thought it was a neat gift. He used it to remove the scales from the fish he caught. With 5 strokes of the comb he could knock off 34 scales. (He counted them.)

How many strokes would it take knock off *at least* 380 scales. Use a conversion factor.

889. Which is smaller? $\frac{4}{7}$ or $\frac{5}{8}$

918. Joe's comb had 65 teeth. After he scaled his fish he noticed that he had lost two-fifths of the teeth in his comb. How many teeth remained?

(Hints: This is a two-step problem. One way to do this problem is first determine how many teeth he lost.)

943. Fill in one word: In an improper fraction the _____?_____ is greater than or equal to the denominator.

950. $\frac{3}{8}$ means $3 \div 8$ which means 3 divided by 8.

$$\frac{\frac{5}{6}}{\frac{4}{5}} = ?$$

Chapter Thirty-two
Estimating Answers

First part: Problems from this chapter

835. Darlene had 99 cans of hair spray. If she used one can each week, roughly how long will those 99 cans last?
   A) 1 year
   B) 2 years
   C) 99 years

Super
Sticky
Hair
Plaster

869. If each can of hair spray costs $4, roughly how much did the 99 cans cost?
   A) $4
   B) $44
   C) $400

875. Darlene applied six coats of CURIE'S GLOW-IN-THE-LIGHT NAIL POLISH to her finger nails. Her hands were now 13 pounds heavier than before she put on the six coats.
   Roughly, how much did each coat weigh?
   A) $\frac{1}{6}$ pound
   B) 1 pound
   C) 2 pounds
   D) $6 \times 13 = 78$ pounds

881. Darlene liked dresses with four buttons.
She called them her "four-button dresses."
She has 52 four-button dresses.
   She decided to replace all the buttons on those dresses with new specially designed buttons.

Darlene

Roughly how many of these new buttons will she need?
A) 200   B) 500   C) 540

Second part: the 𝔐ixed 𝔅ag: a variety of problems from this chapter and previous chapters

414. Joe liked to go fishing. It took his mind off other things. On the weekends he spent eleven-twelfths of his time in his fishing boat. What fraction of his weekend was he not in his boat?

663. Six of Darlene's bridal magazines weigh 5 pounds. She wants to pack 11 magazines on Joe's boat for their next fishing adventure. How much will the magazines weigh? (Use a conversion factor.)

715. Darlene's empty purse weighs $4\frac{1}{4}$ pounds. She packs it with $5\frac{1}{2}$ pounds of nail polish, $9\frac{1}{6}$ pounds of magazines, and $1\frac{1}{8}$ pounds of lipstick. How much will all that weigh?

836. (continuing the previous problem) It's often a good idea to get a rough idea of what the answer will be before you start adding

$$4\frac{1}{4} + 5\frac{1}{2} + 9\frac{1}{6} + 1\frac{1}{8}$$

Then if you make a big mistake, you will be able to catch it. What is a rough estimate of the sum of these four numbers?

867. $2\frac{1}{8}$
  $\overline{}$
  $5\frac{2}{3}$ (If you need a hint, see #950, two pages ago.)

895. What is the square of $3\frac{1}{3}$?

909. What is the square root of $11\frac{1}{9}$?

(Hint: This is a really hard problem unless you were awake when

you did the previous problem.)

917. Joe was going to invent to new hobby for himself. He called it fish-napping. He could sleep while the fishing pole did all the work. He wrote an article called "Fish-napping" for FISHERMAN'S QUARTERLY magazine. They paid him 6¢ for every 4 words. His article was 166 words long. How much was he paid?

the Jelly Bean

The Complete Solutions and Answers

4. $\frac{2}{7} + \frac{3}{7} = \frac{5}{7}$

7. Name a number—let's call it x—so that 15 < x < 16.

You might have written 15½ or 15⅓ or 15⅞ or 15 $\frac{13}{33}$

There are an infinite (unlimited) number of correct answers.

11. Joe got a job as a sign waver in front of Stanthony's PieOne Pizza. He worked 3 hours per day for 17 days and was paid $8 per hour.

The government took one-third of his pay in income taxes. How much did Joe have left?

Joe worked for 51 hours. (3 × 17 = 51)
Joe made $408. (51 hours × $8/hour)
His income tax was $136. (⅓ × 408)
He had $272 left after taxes. (408 – 136)

14. Fred planted a bean. Later that month it was 37" tall. In another week it doubled in height. How tall was it then?

Doubling is the same as multiplying by two.

$$\begin{array}{r} 37 \\ \times\ 2 \\ \hline 74 \end{array}$$

His bean plant became 74" tall.

35. Yes. 5½ is less than 6. Here is a picture:

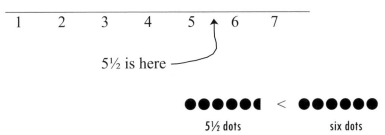

40. Joe likes jelly beans. If one bag of jelly beans cost $3, how much would ten bags cost?

To multiply by 10, you just add a zero. Ten bags would cost $30.

43. Draw a circle and divide it into three equal sectors.

This is often very useful when you have a pizza and three equally hungry people.

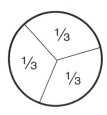

52. Change 198 minutes into hours and minutes.

To change minutes into hours you divide by 60.

$$\begin{array}{r} 3 \ \ \text{R } 18 \\ 60\overline{)\,198} \\ -\underline{180} \\ 18 \end{array}$$

198 minutes is 3 hours and 18 minutes.

55. Change 63" to feet and inches.

To change inches to feet, you divide by 12.

$$\begin{array}{r} 5 \ \ \text{R } 3 \\ 12\overline{)\,63} \\ -\underline{60} \\ 3 \end{array}$$

Sixty-three inches equals 5 feet, three inches.

58. $\dfrac{3}{10} + \dfrac{4}{10} = \dfrac{7}{10}$

60. If doubling means multiplying by 2, what does tripling mean?

Tripling means multiplying by 3.

If you want to multiply by 4, it is called quadrupling.

If you want to multiply by 5, it is called quintupling.

If you want to multiply by 6, you could say it increased sixfold.

Then comes sevenfold, eightfold, ninefold, and so on.

64. 39×28

$$\begin{array}{r} 39 \\ \times\ 28 \\ \hline 312 \\ \underline{78\ \ } \\ 1092 \end{array}$$

68. Suppose a pizza had a 9" radius. Could you put a one-foot ruler on that pizza so that none of the ruler stuck out over the edge of the pizza?

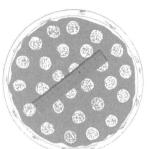

No problem. If a pizza has a radius of 9", it has a diameter of 18". There is plenty of room to put a ruler on top of that pizza.

69. Darlene read in one of her bridal magazines that if you hold your wedding in New York City rather than in Kansas, the total price will triple. She had estimated that marrying Joe in Kansas would cost about $7849. How much would that cost in New York City?

Three times $7849

$$\begin{array}{r} 7849 \\ \times\quad 3 \\ \hline 23547 \end{array}$$

It would cost $23,547. Why does it cost more? One reason is the taxes. In New York City you pay federal income taxes, state income taxes, and city income taxes. One reason that I, the author of the *Life of Fred* books, live in Nevada is that there are no state or city income taxes. With less taxes, I can offer *Fred* books to you more cheaply.

70. If he were seven feet tall and still weighed 37 pounds, he would be very skinny.

88. The three ways that people learn are hearing, writing, and <u>reading</u>.

This was mentioned on page 17 of *Life of Fred: Fractions.*

91. Find the sum of seven, fifteen, and fifty-nine.
Find the sum means "add."

$$\begin{array}{r} 7 \\ 15 \\ +\ 59 \\ \hline 81 \end{array}$$

92. I'm thinking of a number. I'll call that number x.
It is true that x + 7 = 12. What number am I thinking of?

The number I'm thinking of is 5. It is true that 5 + 7 = 12.

There is no other number that works. 4 + 7 ≠ 12.

18 + 7 ≠ 12.

0 + 7 ≠ 12.

≠ means "not equal to."

95. I'm thinking of a number. Call that number x. It is true that 7x = 56.
What is that number? 7x means "seven times x."

That number is 8 since seven times eight equals 56.

100. Is 52 weeks less than a year? (There are approximately 365 days in a
year. Some years have 366 days.)

52 weeks is 364 days since 52 × 7 = 364.

1 year is 365 or 366 days.

Therefore, 52 weeks is less than a year.

small essay

What If Every Year Were 364 Days?

Then every year would be exactly 52 weeks long. If January 1 was on a
Tuesday, then 52 weeks later, January 1 would still be a on a Tuesday.

If your birthday fell on a Saturday, then every year your birthday would be
a on Saturday.

You could use the same calendar every year for the rest of your life.

There is one big giant reason why we don't make every year equal to 364
days. You will learn why when you study astronomy in high school or in college.

end of small essay

101. Think of a number. Call that number x. Is it always true
that x + 0 = x?

Yes. It is always true.

6 + 0 = 6

88 + 0 = 88

567 + 0 = 567

103. Which is smaller: $\frac{1}{3}$ or $\frac{1}{4}$?

One-fourth is less than one-third.

$$\frac{1}{4} < \frac{1}{3}$$

106. I'm thinking of a number. Call that number x.
It is true that 6x = 42. What is that number?

6x means "six times x."

That number is 7 because six times seven equals 42.

113. Change 755 minutes into hours and minutes.
To change minutes into hours you divide by 60.

$$
\begin{array}{r}
12 \quad \text{R } 35 \\
60\overline{)755} \\
-60 \\
\hline
155 \\
-120 \\
\hline
35
\end{array}
$$

Seven hundred fifty-five minutes equals 12 hours and 35 minutes.

125. $\dfrac{5}{9} + \dfrac{2}{9} = \dfrac{7}{9}$

127. Can you think of a number—let's call it y—so that 2y = 7?

y = 0 doesn't work since $2 \times 0 \neq 7$.
y = 1 doesn't work since $2 \times 1 \neq 7$.
y = 2 doesn't work since $2 \times 2 \neq 7$.
y = 3 doesn't work since $2 \times 3 \neq 7$.
y = 4 doesn't work since $2 \times 4 \neq 7$.

But how about y = 3½? It works since $2 \times 3½ = 7$.

Here is why. 3½ is the same as $\dfrac{7}{2}$

$$2 \times 3½ = 2 \times \frac{7}{2} = \frac{2}{1} \times \frac{7}{2} = \frac{14}{2} = 7$$

130. Joe planted a jelly bean. It was June 1st. On June 2nd he planted 2 jelly beans. Then 4 jelly beans on June 3rd. Then 8 jelly beans on June 4th.

He continued. How many did he plant on June 11th?

June 1st	1
June 2nd	2
June 3rd	4
June 4th	8
June 5th	16
June 6th	32
June 7th	64
June 8th	128
June 9th	256
June 10th	512
June 11th	1024

None of Joe's jelly beans grew. Jelly beans aren't really beans. They just have the shape of beans. They are almost pure sugar. If Joe had watered this garden, the beans would have dissolved into a sugar mess. It wouldn't be long before ants would have discovered this. What Joe would have really been growing is a giant ant colony.

133. Each month Joe spends $7 for fishing gear, $308 for rent, $93 for jelly beans, and $5 for food.

Each month Darlene spends $29 for nail polish, $47 for bridal magazines, $340 for rent.

Which of them spends more money?

Joe's spending	Darlene's spending
7	29
308	47
93	+ 340
+ 5	416
413	

Darlene spends three dollars more per month than Joe.

135. I'm thinking of a number—call it y—so that 2y = 9. What is that number? 2y means "two times y."

The number I'm thinking of is 4½ because $2 \times 4\frac{1}{2} = 9$.

$$2 \times 4\frac{1}{2} \ = \ \frac{2}{1} \times \frac{9}{2} \ = \ \frac{18}{2} \ = \ 9$$

141. Fred can walk at 3 mph. In 5 hours he could walk 15 miles.
3 miles per hour × 5 hours = 15 miles.
How far could he walk in 4 hours?

       3 miles per hour × 4 hours = 12 miles.

> When you get to algebra, one of the most famous formulas will
> be $d = rt$. That means that distance equals rate times time.
> 12 miles equals 3 mph × 4 hours.

      Joe was one of Fred's algebra students. When he saw the
formula $d = rt$, he told his girl friend, Darlene, that $d = rt$ is the "dirt
formula."

      Darlene said, "How does $d = rt$ become *dirt*?"

      Joe smiled and said, "Don't you understand? $d = rt$ is distance
iqueals rate times time."

      Darlene told Joe, "*Iqueals* isn't a word. You are thinking of
equals."

      Joe didn't know how to spell *equals*.

150. $\dfrac{5}{17} + \dfrac{8}{17} = \dfrac{13}{17}$

164. $7 \times 8 = 56$
      $0 \times 6 = 0$
      $3{,}782{,}981{,}552 \times 0 = 0$

177. I'm thinking of a number—call it x—such that $x + 3 = 8\frac{1}{4}$. What is
that number?

      That number is 5¼ since $5\frac{1}{4} + 3 = 8\frac{1}{4}$.

188. Fred could fly in his jet at 778 mph.
How far could he go in 8 hours?
Recall: distance equals rate times time. $d = rt$

      778 miles per hour times 8 hours   778
      He could travel 6,224 miles.   ×   8
                                            6224

190. Could you put a circle with a diameter of 14 cm inside a circle with a radius of 9 cm?

That would not be hard to do.

(Centimeters is a measurement in the metric system. Inches is a measurement in the imperial system, which is used only in three countries in the whole world—the U.S.A. being one of them.)

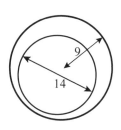

 An *imperial* is also a small pointed beard beneath the lower lip. Many people don't know that.

194. $\frac{1}{5} + \frac{2}{5} = \frac{3}{5}$

197. Write in words 3,782,981,552.

Three billion, seven hundred eighty-two million, nine hundred eighty-one thousand, five hundred fifty-two.

200. $772 + 857$

$$\begin{array}{r} ^1772 \\ + 857 \\ \hline 1629 \end{array}$$

204. Darlene told Joe, "If you were four times richer, you'd be worth $200." How much money does Joe have?

One-fourth of $200 $= 4\overline{)200}^{\,50}$ Joe has $50.

Note that $4 \times 50 = 200$.

205. Think of a number. Call it x. Is it ever possible that 0x = 4?

0x means "zero times x."

$0 \times 0 \neq 4$ $0 \times 1 \neq 4$ $0 \times 4 \neq 4$ $0 \times 234684 \neq 4$

$0 \times \frac{13}{33} \neq 4$ $0 \times$ anything $\neq 4$

For every number x, it will never be true that 0x = 4.

206. Normally, Joe would spend $93 each month on jelly beans. In June his jelly bean costs tripled because he was planting so many jelly beans. What was his jelly bean cost in June?

His costs increased threefold.

$$
\begin{array}{r}
93 \\
\times\ 3 \\
\hline
279
\end{array}
$$

In June, Joe spent $279 on jelly beans.

207. Fred's gift to Alexander was an 18" knife. A sword can be a yard long. (1 yard = 36") The length of that knife is what fraction of the length of a sword? Please reduce your answer as much as possible.

18 is what fraction of 36? It is $\dfrac{18}{36}$

If we divide top and bottom by 2, we get $\dfrac{9}{18}$

If we divide $\dfrac{9}{18}$ by 9 we get $\dfrac{1}{2}$

209. Normally, Joe spends $93 each month for jelly beans. One month they went on sale and he saved $16. How much did Joe spend that month?

He must have spend $16 less than the regular price of $93. He must have spent 93 – 16, which is

$$
\begin{array}{r}
93 \\
-\ 16 \\
\hline
77
\end{array}
$$

He must have spent $77.

212. Darlene watched 111 minutes of television while she was painting her toenails. One-third of that time was commercials. How many minutes were those commercials?

One-third of 111 means

$$
\begin{array}{r}
37 \\
3\overline{)\,111} \\
-\ 9 \\
\hline
21 \\
-\ 21 \\
\hline
0
\end{array}
$$

She watched 37 minutes of commercials.

213. $\dfrac{5}{8} = \dfrac{?}{24}$

We multiplied the bottom by 3, so we will multiply the top by 3.

$\dfrac{5}{8} = \dfrac{15}{24}$

215. Draw a circle with three equal sectors.
     Color in $\dfrac{2}{3}$

216. $\dfrac{1}{5} + \dfrac{2}{5} = \dfrac{3}{5}$

When the bottoms are alike, you add the tops and *copy* the bottom.

218. Fred went to the library and checked out 7 pounds of astronomy books, 28 pounds of physics books, 38 pounds of history books, 13 pounds of poetry books, 45 pounds of math books, and 34 pounds of business books.

He couldn't carry all those books so he sent them by campus mail. The mailman left them on top of his desk. His desk already had a flowerpot (with tulips) on it that weighed 4 pounds. Fred's desk could support 170 pounds without breaking. Would the desk break?

astronomy	7
physics	28
history	38
poetry	13
math	45
business	34
flowerpot	+ 4
	169

Since 169 < 170, his desk didn't break.

219. Which is smaller: $\dfrac{11}{12}$ or $\dfrac{15}{18}$?

$\dfrac{11}{12} = \dfrac{33}{36}$ $\dfrac{15}{18} = \dfrac{30}{36}$ $\dfrac{15}{18}$ is smaller.

220. What is the least common denominator for fractions whose denominators are 12 and 16?

The smallest number that 12 and 16 divide evenly into is 48.

222. Darlene had packed a zillion cherries for a picnic with Joe.

Joe said that he would be happy with $\frac{5}{8}$ of the cherries.

Darlene was on a diet and said she would be happy with $\frac{1}{3}$ of them. They both agreed that they would feed the rest of them to the duck. What fraction of the cherries would the people get?

Joe and Darlene would get $\frac{5}{8} + \frac{1}{3}$ of the cherries.

$$\frac{5}{8} + \frac{1}{3} = \frac{15}{24} + \frac{8}{24} = \frac{23}{24} \qquad \text{(That left } \frac{1}{24} \text{ for the duck.)}$$

223. Write the Roman numerals from 21 to 30.

XXI, XXII, XXIII, XXIV, XXV, XXVI, XXVII, XXVIII, XXIX, XXX

225. Using what you learned from the answer to the previous problem (#650), is ≠ transitive? ≠ means "not equal to."

This question is asking if we know that x ≠ y and we know that y ≠ z, must it *always* be true that x ≠ z?

We know that it is *often* true, but is it always true?

Fred's ingestion (eating) of jelly beans is not equal to Joe's. (Who, except Joe, could eat four pounds of jelly beans each day?) Joe's ingestion of jelly beans is not equal to Darlene's. (Darlene is watching her weight. She wants to fit into her wedding dress. She doesn't eat jelly beans.) So Fred ≠ Joe and Joe ≠ Darlene, but Fred = Darlene (since neither of them eat jelly beans).

≠ is *not* transitive. 0 ≠ 4 and 4 ≠ 0 does not imply 0 ≠ 0.

228. Divide MMLXXXVIII by XXIX. Express your answer in Roman numerals.

$$2088 \div 29 = 72 \qquad\qquad 72 = \text{LXXII}$$

230. $\dfrac{4}{15} + \dfrac{7}{15} = \dfrac{11}{15}$

232. What is the least common denominator for fractions whose denominators are 3, 4, 5, and 6?

The smallest number that 3, 4, 5, and 6 divide evenly into is 60.

234. Room number 234 would probably be on which floor of a building?

Rooms with numbers like 117, 138, 144, 197 are usually on the first floor.

Rooms with numbers like 201, 234, 270, 289 are usually on the second floor.

Rooms with numbers like 803, 825, 888 are usually on the eighth floor.

237. $\dfrac{13}{30} + \dfrac{14}{30} = \dfrac{27}{30} = \dfrac{9}{10}$

238. Betty, Alexander, and Joe ordered a Gallon-size™ carton of french fries at Handy Harry's Hamburgers. It contained 537 fries.
If they shared it equally, how many fries would Joe receive?

He would get one-third of the 537 fries. $\overset{179}{3\overline{)537}}$
He would receive 179 fries.

240. When Joe was fishing in his boat, he played his radio so loudly that all the fish in the water near him died.

An airplane flew over Joe and saw of circle of dead fish that was 300 feet in diameter. How far away could Joe's radio kill fish? (In other words, what was the radius of that circle?)

A radius is one-half of a diameter. Joe's radio was killing fish that were 150' away.

$$
\begin{array}{r}
150 \\
2\overline{)300} \\
-\,2 \\
\hline
10 \\
-\,10 \\
\hline
0 \\
\end{array}
$$

241. Write the Roman numerals for 70, 90, and 2,000.

70 = LXX   90 = XC   2,000 = MM

242. $\frac{3}{4} = \frac{27}{?}$

We multiplied the top by 9, so we will multiply the bottom by 9.

$\frac{3}{4} = \frac{27}{36}$

244. Fred makes $500 per month teaching at KITTENS University. He decides to spend one-fourth of his salary buying two-ounce bars of silver. Those bars cost $25 each. How many bars did he buy?

One-fourth of his salary is one-fourth of $500.

He spent $125 buying silver.

Each bar cost $25. He bought 5 bars.

$$4\overline{)500} \quad \frac{125}{}$$

$$25\overline{)125} \quad \frac{5}{}$$

245. Which is smaller: $\frac{13}{20}$ or $\frac{19}{30}$?

$\frac{13}{20} = \frac{39}{60}$ $\frac{19}{30} = \frac{38}{60}$ $\frac{19}{30}$ is smaller.

246. For every six kernels of corn he would add one jelly bean. Three thousand four hundred sixty-eight kernels of popcorn would require how many jelly beans?

One-sixth of 3,468 kernels

$$6\overline{)3468} \quad \frac{578}{}$$

Joe needed 578 jelly beans to make his popcorn not boring.

247. Darlene also packed a big cherry pie for Joe on their picnic. She cut it into 12 equal pieces. Joe said he wanted one-third of the pie. How many pieces was that?

This is the same as asking $\frac{1}{3} = \frac{?}{12}$ $\frac{1}{3} = \frac{4}{12}$

Joe had 4 pieces.

248. Is one billion $\geq$ one million?

One billion is 1,000,000,000.

One million is 1,000,000.

It is true that one billion $\geq$ one million.

249. A fifth of an hour is how many minutes?

One-fifth of an hour $= \frac{1}{5} \times 60$ minutes $= 5\overline{)60}\ \frac{12}{} = 12$ minutes

250. Suppose we are looking at a bunch of sheep. Is "has more wool" transitive?

Yes. If sheep A has more wool than sheep B, and sheep B has more wool than sheep C, then it must be true that sheep A has more wool than sheep C.

  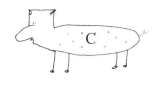

252. $\dfrac{9006}{9888} - \dfrac{7847}{9888} = \dfrac{1159}{9988}$

When you are subtracting fractions with the same bottoms, you just subtract the tops and *copy* the bottom.

255. $\dfrac{3}{8} + \dfrac{3}{8} = \dfrac{6}{8}$ and you reduce this fraction by dividing top and

bottom by 2. $\dfrac{6 \div 2}{8 \div 2} = \dfrac{3}{4}$

257. The letter I can only go to the left of V or X (to indicate subtraction).
The letter X can only go to the left of _L_ or _C_ .
The letter C can only go to the left of _D_ or _M_ .

260. Fred could go 69 mph riding on his train.
How far could he go in 7 hours?

    69 miles per hour times 7 hours
    Fred could go 483 miles.

$$\begin{array}{r} 69 \\ \times\ 7 \\ \hline 483 \end{array}$$

275. Which has the most eggs?

    A) Seven buckets, each holding eight eggs $\quad 7 \times 8 = 56$
    B) Nine lunch boxes, each holding six eggs $\quad 9 \times 6 = 54$
    C) Ten bags, each holding five eggs $\quad 10 \times 5 = 50$

Alternative A) has the most eggs.

279. Darlene liked to read bridal magazines. One article said that for a cheap wedding you should expect to spend $786 for dresses, $655 for music, $88 for invitations, and $19 to rent the groom's tuxedo. The food for the reception is another $2484.

How much is this wedding going to cost?

$$\begin{array}{r} 786 \\ 655 \\ 88 \\ 19 \\ + 2484 \\ \hline 4032 \end{array}$$

The wedding will cost $4,032.

281. $\frac{1}{8} + \frac{5}{8} = \frac{6}{8}$ which reduces to $\frac{3}{4}$

282. Darlene was planning a birthday party for herself. She ordered 167 liters of Sluice, which was to be served to her 644 guests. If all the guests received the same amount, how much would each receive?

In Chapter 15 of *Life of Fred: Fractions*, when 3 pizzas were divided equally among 8 students, each received $\frac{3}{8}$ of a pizza.

Dividing 167 liters equally among 644 guests means that each guest would receive $\frac{167}{644}$ liters.

283. Joe had counted all the cherries before they divided them up. Darlene had packed 240 cherries. Darlene was going to get one-third of the cherries. How many was that?

This is the same as asking $\frac{1}{3} = \frac{?}{240}$

$\frac{1 \times 80}{3 \times 80} = \frac{80}{240}$ Darlene would get 80 cherries.

284. Aneaters normally cost $79, and take a week to deliver. With a special order the price increases sevenfold.

Seven times $79 . . .

$$\begin{array}{r} 79 \\ \times\ 7 \\ \hline 553 \end{array}$$

With a rush order, Joe would be paying $553.

$553

95

286. Reduce $\frac{100}{150}$

$\begin{cases} \text{Divide top and bottom by 10 and we get } \frac{10}{15} \\ \text{Then divide top and bottom by 5 and we get } \frac{2}{3} \end{cases}$

$\begin{cases} \text{Or we could have divided top and bottom by } \frac{100}{150} \text{ by 2 to get } \frac{50}{75} \\ \text{and then divide top and bottom by 25 to get } \frac{2}{3} \end{cases}$

Sometimes there are many ways to reduce a fraction.

288. $\frac{4}{15} + \frac{4}{15} = \frac{8}{15}$

290. 87×76

$$\begin{array}{r} 87 \\ \times\ 76 \\ \hline 522 \\ 609 \\ \hline 6612 \end{array}$$

294.   Start with a really big pizza and cut it into 18 equal slices. If 6 of the slices are eaten, what fraction of the pizza is left?

We start with $\frac{18}{18}$ and we subtract $\frac{6}{18}$

That leaves $\frac{12}{18}$ which reduces to $\frac{2}{3}$ (when you divide top and bottom by 6).

296. Compare $\frac{3}{5}$ and $\frac{14}{20}$

In order to compare two fractions we must make the denominators the same. In this problem we can make both bottoms equal to 20.

$\frac{3}{5} = \frac{12}{20}$ compared with $\frac{14}{20}$ $\frac{12}{20} < \frac{14}{20}$

298. Which is smaller: $\frac{2}{3}$ or $\frac{13}{20}$?

$\frac{2}{3} = \frac{2 \times 20}{3 \times 20} = \frac{40}{60}$ $\frac{13}{20} = \frac{13 \times 3}{20 \times 3} = \frac{39}{60}$ $\frac{13}{20}$ is smaller.

300. 100 is "one hundred."

How would you say 6,000? *Six thousand*

How would you say 7,000,000,000? *Seven billion*

303. (continuing problem 244) Fred bought the silver bars hoping that the price would go up. It went up. He sold the bars for $75 each. How much did receive and what was his profit?

From problem 244, we know he bought 5 bars.

Selling 5 bars at $75 each = 5 × 75

$$\begin{array}{r} 75 \\ \times\ 5 \\ \hline 375 \end{array}$$

Fred received $375.

Since he paid $125 for the bars (from problem 244), his profit was 375 − 125 = $250.

306. $\frac{7}{31} + \frac{8}{31} = \frac{15}{31}$

308. Multiply LXXVII by VII.

77 × 7 = 539   539 = DXXXIX

310. Think of a number. Call that number x. Is it true that x < x + 1?

It is always true.

Suppose the number you thought of was 17. Then x < x + 1 would be 17 < 18.

Suppose the number you thought of was 42. Then x < x + 1 would be 42 < 43.

Suppose the number you thought of was 0. Then x < x + 1 would be 0 < 1.

In every case, x < x + 1 would always be true.

313. Which costs the most?

A) Six chickens, each worth $7.   6 × $7 = $42

B) Three dogs, each worth $13.   3 × $13 = $39

C) Ten rats, each worth $3.   10 × $3 = $30

Alternative A) costs the most.

317. One of Stanthony's really big pizzas is cut into 18 equal slices. Each slice weighs 7 pounds. How much does the whole pizza weigh?

It weighs 18 times as much as a single slice.

$$\begin{array}{r} 18 \\ \times\ 7 \\ \hline 126 \end{array}$$

His really big pizza weighs 126 pounds.

318. Darlene estimated that half of her 644 birthday party guests would bring her gifts that were worth over $300 each. How many of these gifts worth more than $300 did she expect to receive?

One-half of 644 $= \dfrac{1}{2} \times 644 = 2\overline{)644}^{\,322} = 322$ gifts

320. This is question 320. Is 320 a cardinal number or an ordinal number?

Three hundred and twenty is a cardinal number.
This is *not* the 320th question in this book.

321. Compare $\dfrac{3}{4}$ and $\dfrac{2}{3}$

We make both bottoms equal to 12.

$\dfrac{3}{4} = \dfrac{9}{12}$ and $\dfrac{2}{3} = \dfrac{8}{12}$ $\qquad \dfrac{2}{3} < \dfrac{3}{4}$

322. Which is true: $\dfrac{2}{3} < \dfrac{3}{4}$ or $\dfrac{3}{4} < \dfrac{2}{3}$?

Compare with $\qquad \dfrac{2}{3} < \dfrac{3}{4}$

325. Which of these are true and which are false?

$7 < 96$	True. $7 is less than $96.
$7 < 4$	False. I'd rather have $7 than $4.
$7 < 6\frac{1}{2}$	False. When you are $6\frac{1}{2}$ years old, you are not yet 7 years old.

98

327. Darlene owns 56 bottles of nail polish. Twenty-eight of them are red. What fraction of her nail polish bottles are red?

$\frac{28}{56}$ of her nail polish bottles are red.

We could reduce that fraction by dividing top and bottom by 2. That would give us $\frac{14}{28}$ which we could reduce by dividing top and bottom again by 2 which would give us $\frac{7}{14}$ which we could reduce by dividing top and bottom by 7 and get $\frac{1}{2}$

Half of her collection is red.

We could have also done the reducing by recognizing that both 28 and 56 are multiples of 7. Dividing top and bottom by 7 gives us $\frac{4}{8}$ which reduces to $\frac{1}{2}$

329. Which is smaller: $\frac{7}{9}$ or $\frac{9}{11}$?

In order to compare fractions, we need to make the denominators alike. $\frac{7}{9} = \frac{7 \times 11}{9 \times 11} = \frac{77}{99}$ $\frac{9}{11} = \frac{9 \times 9}{11 \times 9} = \frac{81}{99}$ $\frac{7}{9}$ is smaller

331. Divide MMMMCXVI by LXXXIV and express your answer in Roman numerals.

$$\begin{array}{r} 49 \\ 84\overline{)4116} \\ -\ 336 \\ \hline 756 \\ -\ 756 \\ \hline 0 \end{array}$$

49 = XLIX

You can't write 49 as IL because I can only go to the left of V or X.

333. Darlene had packed 240 cherries. Joe was going to get five-eighths of them. How many was that?

This is the same as asking $\frac{5}{8} = \frac{?}{240}$

How much times 8 would give me 240? $8\overline{)240}\ ^{30}$

$\frac{5 \times 30}{8 \times 30} = \frac{150}{240}$ Joe's share was 150 cherries.

334. Darlene sent out 644 birthday party invitations.

Six hundred thirty-six invited people weren't going to her birthday party. What fraction would be attending?

644 − 636 = 8 people would be attending.

Eight people out of 644 is $\dfrac{8}{644}$

$$\dfrac{8}{644} = \dfrac{4}{322} = \dfrac{2}{161}$$

335. Think of a number. Call that number x.

Suppose you know that x − 7 = 14. What is the value of x?

x must be 21 since 21 − 7 = 14.

337. Change $\dfrac{44}{7}$ into a mixed number.

$\dfrac{44}{7}$ means
$$\begin{array}{r} 6\ \text{R2} \\ 7\overline{)\,44} \\ -\underline{42} \\ 2 \end{array}$$
$\dfrac{44}{7} = 6\dfrac{2}{7}$

338. Find the least common multiple (LCM) of 3, 6, and 9.

The LCM of 3, 6, and 9 is the smallest number that 3, 6, and 9 divide evenly into. That number is 18.

340. Name a number—let's call it x—so that 13 < x < 16.

There are many different answers that are possible. There are many different numbers that are larger than 13 and smaller than 16. The two most commonly named are 14 and 15.

Once you learn about fractions, you might also say 14½ or 15½ or 14¼ or 14⅞.

Once you learn about decimals, you might say 14.3 or 15.9896.

In algebra you will learn about square roots. Then you might say that $13 < \sqrt{197} < 16$.

345. Two-sevenths of Joe's boat is filled with fishing equipment. One-seventh of the boat is filled with bottles of Sluice. Three-sevenths of the boat is filled with bags of jelly beans. How much of his boat is occupied by fishing equipment, Sluice, and jelly beans?

$$\dfrac{2}{7} + \dfrac{1}{7} + \dfrac{3}{7} = \dfrac{6}{7}$$

346. Express 230 minutes in hours and minutes.

$$\frac{3 \ R \ 50}{60)\ 230}$$

230 minutes = 3 hours, 50 minutes

347. Change $\frac{638}{8}$ into a mixed number.

$$\begin{array}{r} 79 \ R \ 6 \\ 8)\ 638 \\ -56 \\ \hline 78 \\ -72 \\ \hline 6 \end{array}$$

$$\frac{638}{8} = 79\frac{6}{8} = 79\frac{3}{4}$$

348. Joe had 18 bottles of Sluice and he was assigned to pour that evenly into 30 glasses. How much should go into each glass?

When you divide 18 bottles among 30 glasses, each glass receives $\frac{18}{30}$ of a bottle. $\frac{18}{30} = \frac{9}{15} = \frac{3}{5}$

Pour three-fifths of a bottle into each glass.

349. On the day Fred bought the silver, he noticed that gold was 58 times more expensive than silver. A two-ounce bar of silver was $25. How much would a two-ounce bar of gold cost?

It would cost 58 times as much. It would cost $1,450.

$$\begin{array}{r} 58 \\ \times 25 \\ \hline 290 \\ 116 \\ \hline 1450 \end{array}$$

351. On one fishing trip Joe caught 4 salmon and 16 guppies. What fraction of his catch were guppies?

Sixteen out of 20 fish were guppies. $\frac{16}{20}$ which reduces to $\frac{4}{5}$

Joe put the guppies in a pail of water. When he got home, he transferred them to his aquarium. He sold the salmon to his friends.

The word *salmon* has a silent *l* in it.

101

353. Think of a number. Call that number x. Is it always true
x + 7 = 7 + x?

        Yes. It is always true.

        Suppose the number you thought of was 4. Then $4 + 7 = 7 + 4$.

        Suppose the number you thought of was 50. Then $50 + 4 = 4 + 50$.

355. Joe packed 56 bags of jelly beans in his backpack. On the one-hour walk, he ate 21 of those bags. What fraction had he eaten? Please reduce your answer as much as possible.

        He ate $\dfrac{21}{56}$ of the bags.

        Here is where knowing your multiplication tables really helps speed things up. If you didn't know your tables and just had a calculator, you would have to try dividing by various numbers to see if anything worked.

        Knowing your tables, you would recognize that 21 and 56 are both multiples of 7.

        Take $\dfrac{21}{56}$ and divide top and bottom by 7 and get $\dfrac{3}{8}$

        Joe had eaten three-eighths of the bags that he had packed.

357. To make a really big pizza, Stanthony shoveled $\dfrac{3}{19}$ of the cheese pile into a wheelbarrow and brought it into the kitchen. What fraction of the cheese pile was left outside?

        We start with a whole cheese pile: $\dfrac{19}{19}$

        We remove $\dfrac{3}{19}$

        That leaves $\dfrac{16}{19}$ of the cheese pile. $\dfrac{19}{19} - \dfrac{3}{19} = \dfrac{16}{19}$

359. Joe caught 88 fish. Three-fourths of them had blue fins. How many was that?

        This is the same as asking $\dfrac{3}{4} = \dfrac{?}{88}$

        We need to multiply the bottom by 22 since $4\overline{)\,88}^{\,22}$

        $\dfrac{3 \times 22}{4 \times 22} = \dfrac{66}{88}$ 66 of the fish that Joe caught had blue fins.

360. What is the LCM of 4, 8, and 16?

The smallest number that 4, 8, and 16 divide evenly into is 16.

361. Does your calculator use ordinal numbers?

It would be tough to type "second" or "54th" into a calculator.

It uses cardinal numbers, but it also uses numbers that are *not* cardinal numbers. If you type 8.5 into a calculator, you are using decimal numbers, which you'll learn about in *Life of Fred: Decimals and Percents*. In that book you will learn that 8.5 means $8\frac{5}{10}$ which equals 8½.

Cardinal numbers are numbers that are used to *count* things like people or dogs or telephones or shirts. You can't have 8½ people. The cardinal numbers are {0, 1, 2, 3, 4, 5, . . .}. The three periods (. . .) mean "etc."

Numbers like 8½ are used to *measure* things. It might take you 8½ hours to build a greenhouse. The greenhouse could be 8½ feet wide.

363.

8:00 A.M.	BEGINNING ALGEBRA
9:00 A.M.	ADVANCED ALGEBRA
10:00 A.M.	GEOMETRY
11:00 A.M.	TRIG
12 M.	CALCULUS
1:00 P.M.	TRIP TO THE LIBRARY

What fraction of his classes does he teach before noon?

He teaches four classes before noon and one class in the afternoon.

He teaches $\frac{4}{5}$ of his classes before noon.

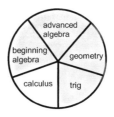

365. What's the least common denominator for $\frac{1}{15}$ and $\frac{1}{20}$?

If you just multiplied 15 × 20, which is 300, that would be common denominator, but it wouldn't be the *least* common denominator.

The least common denominator is 60.

Both 15 and 20 divide evenly into 60, and no smaller number works.

366. LCM stands for least common multiple .
     LCD stands for least common denominator .

367. (continuing problem 279) Darlene saves $12/month. How many months will she have to save to afford her wedding?

How many times does 12 go into $4,032?

$$
\begin{array}{r}
336 \\
12\overline{)4032} \\
-36 \\
\hline
43 \\
-36 \\
\hline
72 \\
-72 \\
\hline
0
\end{array}
$$

She will have to save for 336 months.

368. Express 230 minutes in hours.

$$
\begin{array}{r}
3 \\
60\overline{)230} \\
-180 \\
\hline
50
\end{array}
$$

230 minutes $= 3\,\dfrac{50}{60} = 3\,\dfrac{5}{6}$ hours

370. Fred had $1,935.06 in his checking account. He wrote a check for $1,935.06. How much did Fred have left in his account?

He had no money left in his account. $0.

For any number—call it x—it is always true that $x - x = 0$.

372. How would you write 90,000 in Roman numerals?

This is hard. We know that M = 1,000. So 90,000 might be written as MMMMMMMMMMMMMMMMMMMMMMMMMMMMMM MMMMMMMMMMMMMMMMMMMMMMMMMMMMMMMM MMMMMMMMMMMMMMMMMMMMMMMMMMMM.

I would hate to think what it would be like to write a billion (a million thousands) in Roman numerals. Writing a million Ms would take a long time.

374. $\frac{1}{3} + \frac{3}{5} =$?

$$\frac{1}{3} = \frac{5}{15} \qquad \frac{3}{5} = \frac{9}{15} \qquad \frac{5}{15} + \frac{9}{15} = \frac{14}{15}$$

376. Joe had 21 empty jelly bean bags. He took one of them and blew it up, twisted the end, and popped it by clapping his hands together.

This frightened the birds in the trees. They flew away.

He did it twice more.

What fraction of the empty bags had he popped?

He had popped 3 bags out of 21. That's $\frac{3}{21}$ which reduces to $\frac{1}{7}$ when you divide top and bottom by 3.

378. Kingie's picture sold for $602. Fred's picture sold for one-seventh of what Kingie's picture sold for. What was the selling price of Fred's picture?

One-seventh of 602

$$\begin{array}{r} 86 \\ 7\overline{)602} \\ -\,56 \\ \hline 42 \\ -\,42 \\ \hline 0 \end{array}$$

Fred's picture sold for $86.

380. Change $\frac{604}{7}$ into a mixed number.

$$\begin{array}{r} 86\ \text{R}\ 2 \\ 7\overline{)604} \\ -\,56 \\ \hline 44 \\ -\,42 \\ \hline 2 \end{array} \qquad \frac{604}{7} = 86\,\frac{2}{7}$$

381. Your piggy bank has 39,741 pennies in it. (It's a big piggy bank.) Is 39,741 a cardinal or an ordinal number?

Cardinal numbers are used to count things like pennies or cars or pencils.

39,741 is a cardinal number.

382. 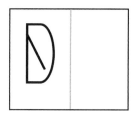 will become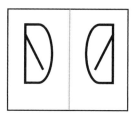

The resulting picture has a line of symmetry along the fold.

383. If Darlene spent $\frac{3}{8}$ of her money on clothes and nail polish, what fraction did she have left to spend on other things (such as rent, food, and books)?

She had $\frac{5}{8}$ of her money to spend on those other things.

$$\frac{3}{8} + \frac{5}{8} = \frac{8}{8} = 1$$

384. Darlene saw a sale on dresses. "All dresses $24!!!!!" She also noticed: "No sales tax if you pay cash!!!!!"

Darlene borrowed $384 from her mom and rushed to the store. How many dresses could she buy?

How many 24's are in 384?

$$\begin{array}{r} 16 \\ 24\overline{)384} \\ -24 \\ \hline 144 \\ -144 \\ \hline 0 \end{array}$$

She could buy 16 dresses.

385. $\frac{5}{6} - \frac{3}{4} = \frac{10}{12} - \frac{9}{12} = \frac{1}{12}$ One-twelfth of a pound was left.

386. $\frac{2}{3} \times \frac{7}{8} = \frac{14}{24}$ By General Rule #1, we should reduce fractions in our answers as much as possible. $\frac{14}{24} = \frac{7}{12}$

387. Change $6\frac{2}{3}$ into an improper fraction.

The hard way: $6\frac{2}{3} = \frac{18}{3} + \frac{2}{3} = \frac{20}{3}$

The easy way: $6\frac{2}{3} = \frac{20}{3}$ *3 times 6 . . . plus 2*

388. Which is smaller: $\frac{2}{7}$ or $\frac{3}{8}$?

To compare two fractions we make their denominators alike.

$$\frac{2}{7} = \frac{16}{56} \qquad \frac{3}{8} = \frac{21}{56} \qquad \frac{2}{7} < \frac{3}{8}$$

392. When I want to add $\frac{1}{4}$ and $\frac{2}{5}$ do I need to find the LCM of 1 and 2 or do I need to find the LCM of 4 and 5?

I need to find the common denominator of $\frac{1}{4}$ and $\frac{2}{5}$ so I need to find the LCM of 4 and 5, which is 20.

393. The circumference is 18 inches. Three times the diameter is roughly equal to the circumference. That means that the diameter is roughly one-third of the circumference.

One-third of 18 $= \frac{1}{3} \times 18 = 6$ The diameter is roughly 6".

395. If Joe had popped 3 of the 21 empty bags, what fraction of the empty bags had he not popped?

He had not popped 18 out of the 21 bags. That's $\frac{18}{21}$

This fraction reduces to $\frac{6}{7}$ when you divide top and bottom by 3.

397. One day is what fraction of 50 years? (Assume 365 days = 1 year.)

We need to have everything in the same units.
50 years = 50 × 365 days = 18,250 days

Darlene's wedding day is about $\frac{1}{18250}$ of her whole married life.

399. $\frac{11}{15} - \frac{2}{9} = $?

The hardest part is finding the least common multiple (LCM) of the denominators. The 15 is 3×5. The 9 is 3×3. We want something that is divisible by 5 and is divisible by 3×3. The smallest number that works is 45.

$$\frac{11}{15} - \frac{2}{9} = \frac{33}{45} - \frac{10}{45} = \frac{23}{45}$$

401. When you double the height of a child (or a moose or a tree or a house) you increase its weight by about eightfold. That is because you are doubling the height, doubling the width, and doubling the depth.

If a three-foot tall dog weighed 29 pounds, what would its expected weight be when it was six-feet tall?

It would weigh about 8 times as much.

$$\begin{array}{r} 29 \\ \times\ 8 \\ \hline 232 \end{array}$$

The dog would weigh about 232 pounds.

414. Joe liked to go fishing. It took his mind off other things. On the weekends he spent eleven-twelfths of his time in his fishing boat. What fraction of his weekend was he not in his boat?

One-twelfth of his weekends was spent on land. $\dfrac{11}{12} + \dfrac{1}{12} = 1$

416. What's the least common denominator for $\dfrac{1}{18}$ and $\dfrac{1}{180}$?

The smallest number that both 18 and 180 divide evenly into is 180.

417. How many whole numbers are less than 3?

The whole numbers are {0, 1, 2, 3, 4, 5, 6, 7, ... }.
There are three whole numbers that are less than 3.
They are 0, 1, and 2.

418. The least common denominator for $\dfrac{1}{28}$ and $\dfrac{1}{42}$ is 84.

What is the least common multiple of 28 and 42?

Do you wish that all math questions were this easy? The least common multiple of denominators is called the least common denominator. The least common multiple of 28 and 42 is 84.

420. If Fred could read three books in a week, how many could he read in 52 weeks? He could read 3 books times 52.

$$\begin{array}{r} 52 \\ \times\ 3 \\ \hline 156 \end{array}$$

He could read 156 books in 52 weeks.

422. After she spent $\frac{1}{3}$ of her time handing cherries, $\frac{1}{3}$ of her time explaining, and $\frac{1}{6}$ of her time picking up pits, how much time did she have left?

$$\frac{1}{3} + \frac{1}{3} + \frac{1}{6} = \frac{2}{6} + \frac{2}{6} + \frac{1}{6} = \frac{5}{6}$$

Darlene had spent five-sixths of her time doing these three things. She had one-sixth of her time left over.

424. (continuing problem 351) Salmon weigh a lot more than guppies. If each of the salmon Joe caught weighed 9 pounds, and each of the guppies weighed one ounce, then . . .

A) How much did all the salmon weigh?

4 salmon each weighing 9 pounds = 36 pounds of salmon

B) How many pounds did the guppies weigh?

16 guppies each weighing one ounce = 16 ounces of guppies, which is one pound

C) What was the total weight of his catch?

36 pounds of salmon plus 1 pound of guppies = 37 pounds

D) What fraction of the total weight were the guppies?

1 pound out of a total of 37 pounds is $\frac{1}{37}$

425. What's the least common denominator for $\frac{1}{16}$ and $\frac{1}{32}$?

The smallest number that both 16 and 32 divide into is 32.

427. Fred could run at 7 mph. In 3 hours he could run 21 miles.
By the d = rt formula, $21 = 7 \times 3$.

How far could Fred run in 8 hours? (We are assuming he doesn't get tired.)

7 miles per hour × 8 hours = 56 miles
By the d = rt formula, 56 miles = 7 mph times 8 hours.

429. $\frac{1}{4} + \frac{2}{5} = ?$

$$\frac{1}{4} = \frac{5}{20} \qquad \frac{2}{5} = \frac{8}{20} \qquad \frac{5}{20} + \frac{8}{20} = \frac{13}{20}$$

430. 97 × 47

$$\begin{array}{r} 97 \\ \times\ 47 \\ \hline 679 \\ 388 \\ \hline 4559 \end{array}$$

432. What's the least common denominator for $\frac{1}{10}$ and $\frac{1}{15}$?

150 is a common denominator, but it is not the least common denominator. The least common denominator is 30.

433. It does not have a line of symmetry.
If we draw it with a wet pen on a piece of paper

and then try to fold it

we do not get the original diagram.

Two things spoil the symmetry.

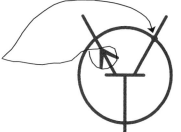

434. Change $\frac{39}{6}$ into a mixed number.

$$\begin{array}{r} 6\ \text{R}3 \\ 6)\overline{\,39} \\ -36 \\ \hline 3 \end{array} \qquad \frac{39}{6} = 6\frac{3}{6} = 6\frac{1}{2}$$

436. When she got to the store, she was delighted. The dresses were all marked $12 (instead of $24). How many dresses could she buy?

$$12\overline{)384} \qquad \frac{384}{12} = 32 \qquad \text{She could buy 32 dresses.}$$

Above the division: 32

437. Is *seventh* a cardinal number?

No. It is an ordinal number.

438. Joe didn't know what to do with the $\frac{3}{4}$ of a pound of bad cheese. He put $\frac{3}{8}$ lb. of it into his scrapbook. The rest he fed to his fish. How much did it feed to his fish?

$$\frac{3}{4} - \frac{3}{8} = \frac{6}{8} - \frac{3}{8} = \frac{3}{8} \qquad \text{He fed } \frac{3}{8} \text{ lb. to his fish.}$$

440. Which weighs the most?

A) 9 five-ounce oranges $9 \times 5 = 45$ ounces

B) 8 six-ounce peaches $8 \times 6 = 48$ ounces

C) 4 eleven-ounce coconuts $4 \times 11 = 44$ ounces

Alternative B) weighs the most.

441. Twenty minutes is what fraction of an hour?

20 minutes is what fraction of 60 minutes?

$$\frac{20}{60} = \frac{1}{3} \qquad \text{Twenty minutes is one-third of an hour.}$$

442. After Joe caught his first fish, he celebrated by drinking $\frac{4}{5}$ of a cup of Sluice.

After his second fish, he drank $\frac{2}{3}$ cup of Sluice.

After his third fish, he drank $\frac{1}{2}$ cup Sluice.

In all that celebration how much Sluice did he drink?

$$\frac{4}{5} + \frac{2}{3} + \frac{1}{2} = \frac{24}{30} + \frac{20}{30} + \frac{15}{30} = \frac{59}{30} = 30\overline{)59}$$

1 R29

−30

29

He drank $1\frac{29}{30}$ cups of Sluice.

444. Your answer may be different than mine. That's okay.
I look at < and notice that the little end is on the left.

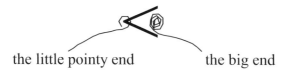

the little pointy end   the big end

This is also true for greater than. > The little pointy end points to the smaller number.

446. The least common denominator of $\frac{1}{360}$ and $\frac{1}{150}$ is 1,800.

What is the least common denominator of $\frac{7}{360}$ and $\frac{117}{150}$?

When you are looking for the least common denominator, it doesn't matter what the numerators are. The least common denominator of $\frac{7}{360}$ and $\frac{117}{150}$ is also 1,800.

447. What is the smallest whole number?
The whole numbers are 0, 1, 2, 3, 4, 5. . . .
The smallest whole number is 0.

448. No it doesn't. If you draw it with a wet pen

and fold the paper along a vertical line

you get 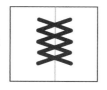 which is not the same as the original picture.

Folding the paper along a horizontal line ↔ or a diagonal line ↘ also doesn't work.

112

450. Room 765 is probably on which floor of a building?
Rooms 133, 147, 175 are on the first floor.
Rooms 250, 272, 299 are on the second floor.
Room 765 is on the seventh floor.

451. He whistled 88 notes every minute. It took him seven minutes to walk home. How many notes did he whistle on that trip?

$$7 \times 88 = 616 \qquad \begin{array}{r} {}^{5}88 \\ \times\ 7 \\ \hline 616 \end{array}$$

He whistled 616 notes.

453. How many years will she have to save? In other words, how many years is 336 months?

$$\begin{array}{r} 28 \\ 12\overline{)336} \\ -24 \\ \hline 96 \\ -96 \\ \hline 0 \end{array}$$

Darlene will have to save for 28 years for her wedding.

455.

If we fold  we get

The original picture was *not* symmetrical along the fold line.
(Of course, the *resulting* picture does have symmetry along the fold line.)

456. What is four-fifths of $3\frac{3}{4}$?

Of often means multiply. $\quad \dfrac{4}{5} \times 3\dfrac{3}{4} = \dfrac{\overset{1}{\cancel{4}}}{\underset{1}{\cancel{5}}} \times \dfrac{\overset{3}{\cancel{15}}}{\underset{1}{\cancel{4}}} = 3$

457. If you lined up the teachers at KITTENS University from shortest to tallest, Fred would be first in the line. Is first a cardinal number?

No it is not. First is an ordinal number. So are second, third, fourth, fifth, and so on.

459. There are six chances in seven that he's going to have serious health problems because of his diet. Express six chances in seven as a fraction.

$$\text{Six chances in seven} = \frac{6}{7}$$

461. Joe spends $413 each month. Each month his mother gives him $43. He gets $293 from the government. He gets $8 from selling fish. He gets $69 from waving a sign in front of Stanthony's pizza place.

How much will Joe save each month?

How much will he save each year?

How much will he save in a century?

His income is 43 + 293 + 8 + 69, which is $413.

His expenses are $413.

He saves $0 each month, $0 each year, and $0 each century.

463. $\dfrac{4}{5} - \dfrac{3}{4} = \dfrac{16}{20} - \dfrac{15}{20} = \dfrac{1}{20}$

One-twentieth of a gallon was left in the tank.

466. If the dresses were free, she could buy $\dfrac{384}{0}$ How many is this?

Division by zero makes a real mess. The answer is bigger than 1,000 dresses. Bigger than 3,298,992,005,442 dresses. Bigger than any number you can name.

Logic lesson: *If it is bigger than any number, then it can't be a number.*

$\dfrac{384}{0}$ is not a number. There is no answer.

467. A rectangle measured $4\frac{2}{3}$ by $7\frac{1}{6}$ miles. It was a big field. How many square miles was it?

$$A = \ell w = 4\frac{2}{3} \times 7\frac{1}{6} = \frac{14}{3} \times \frac{43}{6} = \frac{602}{18} \qquad 18\overline{)602} \;\; {}^{33\ R\ 8}$$

$$A = 33\frac{8}{18} = 33\frac{4}{9} \text{ square miles}$$

114

468. If every jar of peanuts contained 972 peanuts, how many peanuts would be in 8 jars?

$$\begin{array}{r} 972 \\ \times\ 8 \\ \hline 7776 \end{array}$$

There are 7,776 peanuts in eight jars.

Seven thousand, seven hundred seventy-six peanuts.

470. Which has the greatest volume?

    A) Seven garbage cans, each holding 6 gallons $7 \times 6 = 42$

    B) Ten garbage cans, each holding 5 gallons $10 \times 5 = 50$

    C) Five garbage cans, each holding 9 gallons. $5 \times 9 = 45$

Alternative B has the greatest volume of garbage.

472. What is the least common denominator for fractions whose denominators are 5, 10, and 15?

    The smallest number that 5, 10, and 15 divide into evenly is 30.

473. The word *of* between two numbers often mean multiply.

    What is three-fifths of two-thirds?

$$\frac{3}{5} \times \frac{2}{3} = \frac{6}{15} = \frac{2}{5}$$

475. 100 is "one hundred."

How would you say 3,000?   *Three thousand*

How would you say 10,000?   *Ten thousand*

How would you say 5,000,000?   *Five million*

477. When Darlene got home with 1,488 dresses, she noticed that one-third of them had broken zippers. How many had broken zippers?

One-third of 1488 $= \frac{1}{3} \times 1488$ $3\overline{)1488} = 496$ 496 had broken zippers.

479. When the garbage truck came to empty the dumpster, $\frac{5}{16}$ of a gallon of water had leaked out onto the street. How much was still in the dumpster?

$$\frac{3}{4} - \frac{5}{16} = \frac{12}{16} - \frac{5}{16} = \frac{7}{16}$$

Seven-sixteenths of a gallon was left in the dumpster.

480. Name a number—let's call it x—so that $400 < x < 900$.

There are lots of possibilities. You might have written 401 or 402, or 538 or 889 or even 457½.

481. What is the perimeter of a rectangle that is $4\frac{2}{3}$ by $7\frac{1}{6}$ miles?

$$4\frac{2}{3} + 7\frac{1}{6} + 4\frac{2}{3} + 7\frac{1}{6}$$

$$= 4\frac{4}{6} + 7\frac{1}{6} + 4\frac{4}{6} + 7\frac{1}{6} \ = \ 22\frac{10}{6} \ = \ 22\frac{6}{6} + \frac{4}{6}$$

$$= 23\frac{4}{6} \ = \ 23\frac{2}{3} \text{ miles}$$

482. What is the least common denominator for fractions whose denominators are 2, 4, 6, 8, and 10?

The smallest number that 2, 4, 6, 8, and 10 divide evenly into is 120.

484. Joe had caught LXXXVIII fish. He could sell them for VII¢ each. How much could he get for those fish? (¢ means cents.)

88×7

$$\begin{array}{r} 88 \\ \times\ 7 \\ \hline 616 \end{array}$$

He could get DCXVI¢ for his fish.

(Later when we get to decimals, we will learn that 616¢ = $6.16.)

486. IX Romans found CCCXXXIII gold pieces and divided the coins equally among them. How many gold pieces did each Roman receive? Give your answer in Roman numerals.

This is the same as asking how many times 9 divides into 333.

$$\begin{array}{r} 37 \\ 9\overline{)333} \\ -27 \\ \hline 63 \\ -63 \\ \hline 0 \end{array}$$

Each Roman received XXXVII gold pieces.

488. Express 324 seconds in minutes and seconds.

$$\begin{array}{r} 5\ R\ 24 \\ 60\overline{)324} \\ -300 \\ \hline 24 \end{array}$$

324 seconds = 5 minutes, 24 seconds

490. That's the same as asking how many $\frac{1}{4}$ are there in 36.

If you want to know how many 2's are in 10, you compute $10 \div 2$.

$36 \div \frac{1}{4} = 36 \times \frac{4}{1} = 144$.   Darlene could serve 144 guests.

492. He unrolled 280 inches of toilet paper. How many feet and inches is that?

$$280 \text{ inches} \times \frac{1 \text{ foot}}{12 \text{ inches}} = \frac{280}{12} \qquad 12\overline{)280} \quad \begin{array}{c} 23 \text{ R } 4 \end{array}$$

$280" = 23' \, 4"$

493. Are sticking jelly beans in your mouth and then chewing them commutative?

You can't first chew them and *then* stick them in your mouth! Those two operations are not commutative.

495. If Fred could read and answer a piece of fan mail in 8 minutes, how long would it take him to read and answer a dozen pieces of fan mail?

It would take him twelve times as long. $8 \times 12 = 96$
It would take him 96 minutes.

497. What is the least common denominator for fractions whose denominators are IX and XV? Give your answer in Roman numerals.

IX = 9   XV = 15   The least common denominator is 45.
The least common denominator will be XLV.

498. Six of the 1,488 dresses that Darlene bought were wedding dresses.

What fraction of the dresses that Darlene bought were wedding dresses?

$$\frac{6}{1488} = \frac{3}{744} = \frac{1}{248}$$

dividing top and bottom by 2   dividing top and bottom by 3

117

500.

 becomes

This is not the same as the original picture. It does not have symmetry along that diagonal line.

502. Is $\frac{1}{6}$ less than $\frac{1}{4}$?

Yes. $\frac{1}{6} < \frac{1}{4}$

504. What is the least common denominator for fractions whose denominators are 4, 6, and 10?

    The smallest number that 4, 6, and 10 divide into evenly is 60.

506. Those 88 fish had eaten 11 pounds of bait before they were caught. If all the fish had eaten the same amount, how much did each fish eat?

    If 11 pounds is shared equally among 88 fish, each fish would have eaten $\frac{11}{88}$ pounds.

    We reduce this fraction by dividing top and bottom by 11.

$$\frac{11 \div 11}{88 \div 11} = \frac{1}{8}$$ Each fish enjoyed one-eighth of a pound of bait.

508. A barrel of oil is 42 gallons. One gallon is 4 quarts. How many quarts are in a barrel?

$$\frac{42 \text{ gallons}}{1} \times \frac{4 \text{ quarts}}{1 \text{ gallon}} = 168 \text{ quarts}$$

510. How many feet is 280"?

$$280 \text{ inches} \times \frac{1 \text{ foot}}{12 \text{ inches}} = \frac{280}{12}$$

$$12\overline{)280} \quad \begin{array}{c} 23 \text{ R } 4 \end{array}$$

$$280 \text{ inches} = 23\frac{4}{12} \text{ feet} = 23\frac{1}{3} \text{ feet}$$

That's a lot of toilet paper to blow your nose and wipe your eyes.

512. The diameter of Tree Circle is 6 miles. The circumference is about 18 miles.

513. A bunch of people are sitting on a long bench. Some of them are sitting right next to each other. Is "sitting right next to" transitive?

No. If, for example, Fred is sitting right next to Betty and Betty is sitting right next to Alexander, then Fred couldn't be sitting next to Alexander.

514. Which of these is smaller: $\frac{5}{12}$ or $\frac{2}{5}$?

$$\frac{5}{12} = \frac{25}{60} \qquad \frac{2}{5} = \frac{24}{60} \qquad \frac{2}{5} < \frac{5}{12}$$

515.

Only comes in
multiples of 8

Only comes in
multiples of 10

The least common multiple (LCM) of 8 and 10 is 40. With 40 people at the dinner reception all the plates and mugs will be used with none left over.

516. Putting 4 bottles followed by 3 bottles gives a total of 7 bottles. Putting 3 bottles followed by 4 bottles also gives a total of 7 bottles.

$4 + 3 = 3 + 4$. This illustrates B) Addition is commutative. In algebra we will say that the commutative law for addition is $a + b = b + a$.

518. Fred could go 19 mph in his yacht.
How far could he go in 7 hours?
Using d = rt, $19 \times 7 = 133$ miles.

> We need to note that the speed of ships is not normally measured in miles per hour, but in knots. One knot is a little bit faster than one mph. Once you get to *Life of Fred: Decimals and Percents*, we will be able to say that one knot is roughly equal to 1.15 mph. We can't say that now, because you haven't studied decimals yet.

> The reason we could say miles per hour is that Fred put wheels on his yacht and was driving it down the street.

520. In the PieOne kitchen Fred had 6 pounds of hamburger. He was supposed to spread that evenly on 8 pizzas. How much would each pizza receive?

$$\frac{6}{8} = \frac{3}{4}$$ Each pizza would receive $\frac{3}{4}$ of a pound of hamburger.

522. (continuing problem 508) Darlene was going to order a barrel of salad oil for her wedding reception. Fill in this chart:

salad oil available	each guest uses	number of servings
168 quarts	4 quarts	$\frac{168}{4} = 42$
168 quarts	2 quarts	$\frac{168}{2} = 84$
168 quarts	1 quarts	$\frac{168}{1} = 168$
168 quarts	0 quarts	$\frac{168}{0}$ = If none of the guests used any salad oil, then Darlne could serve an unlimited number of guests at her wedding. She decided to serve a salad oil that no one liked.

524. In Roman numerals, the letter X can only go in front of L or C .

526. Darlene has box that is 4' × 6'. What is the size of the largest round pizza that she could put in that box?

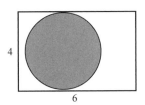

The four-foot width of the box is what is important in this problem. It doesn't matter if the box were 6 feet or 60 feet long.

The pizza could be at most 4 feet across. The diameter of the pizza could be 4 feet at most. (The radius could be 2 feet at most.)

527. Express 324 seconds in minutes.

$$\begin{array}{r} 5 \ R\ 24 \\ 60\overline{)324} \\ -\ 300 \\ \hline 24 \end{array}$$

324 seconds $= 5\frac{24}{60}$ minutes $= 5\frac{2}{5}$ minutes

530. She estimates that there is two chances in ten that he will propose to her before they graduate from college. Express this as a fraction.

Two chances in ten means $\frac{2}{10}$ which reduces to $\frac{1}{5}$

533. Convert 4 feet, 3 inches to inches.

4 feet $\times \dfrac{12\ \text{inches}}{1\ \text{foot}} = 48$ inches.

4 feet, 3 inches $= 48$ inches $+ 3$ inches $= 51$ inches

535. If the radius of a circle is 5 meters, what is its approximate circumference?

If the radius is 5 meters, the diameter is 10 meters. Then the circumference is roughly 30 meters.

537. The diameter of Tree Circle is 6 miles. What is the approximate circumference if we multiply by $3\frac{1}{7}$?

$$6 \times 3\frac{1}{7} = \frac{6}{1} \times \frac{22}{7} = \frac{132}{7} = \begin{array}{r} 18\ R\ 6 \\ 7\overline{)132} \end{array} = 18\frac{6}{7} \text{ miles}$$

540. Fred has 16 pencils. How many more would he need in order to have a gross of pencils. (Hint: one gross = 144.)

To go from 16 to 144, we need to subtract.

$$\begin{array}{r} 144 \\ -\ 16 \\ \hline 128 \end{array}$$

Fred would need 128 more pencils.

542. Is putting on pink polish followed by purple polish commutative?

If you put on pink polish and then purple polish, your toenails will look purple.

If you put on purple polish and then pink polish, your toenails will look pink.

These two operations are *not* commutative because the final results are not the same.

543. When Joe was out fishing in his boat, he once accidentally dropped a purple jelly bean into the water. Joe liked purple jelly beans because they made his tongue purple.

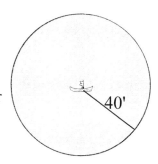

This jelly bean made the water around the boat purple. Forty feet in every direction the water was purple. What was the diameter of that purple circle?

The purple circle had a radius of 40 feet. Its diameter was 80 feet.

544. Darlene wanted to make a new color nail polish. She combined $2\frac{3}{4}$ ounces of blue polish with $3\frac{7}{8}$ ounces of brown polish. How many ounces did she create?

$$2\frac{3}{4} + 3\frac{7}{8} \qquad\qquad 2\frac{3}{4} = 2\frac{6}{8}$$

$$+\ \underline{\qquad 3\frac{7}{8} = 3\frac{7}{8} \qquad}$$

$$5\frac{13}{8} = 5 + 1\frac{5}{8} = 6\frac{5}{8}$$

She created $6\frac{5}{8}$ ounces of polish.

545. Is the number of Roman soldiers in the previous problem a cardinal number or an ordinal number?

    When you count the number of things in any set, you use the cardinal numbers. Nine is a cardinal number.

    The number of Roman soldiers in my dining room is a cardinal number. Zero is a cardinal number.

    The number of stars you can see on a clear dark night is a cardinal number. It is about 4,000.

    The number of members of this infinite set $\{2, 4, 6, 8, 10, 12 \ldots \}$ is a cardinal number. In college mathematics we will name this number. **Stop! I, your reader, want to know now! I don't want to wait. What is the cardinality of $\{2, 4, 6, 8, 10 \ldots \}$?** Okay. This won't make a lot of sense, but the cardinal number of $\{2, 4, 6, 8, 10, 12 \ldots \}$ is $\aleph_0$ (pronounced aleph-null where aleph almost rhymes with *olive*). Aleph-null is the smallest infinite cardinal number. We have got bigger ones. One reason to become a mathematician is all the wild surprises that come in later mathematics—once you get beyond learning the multiplication tables. **Wait! I, your reader, know my multiplication tables. I know $7 \times 9 = 63$. When do I start to see the wild surprises?** I have just told you how many even numbers there are. There are $\aleph_0$ of them. There are also $\aleph_0$ odd numbers. There are aleph-null fractions $\{1/2, 1/3, 2/3, 1/4, 3/4, 1/5, 2/5, 3/5, 4/5, 1/6 \ldots \}$. You now know more than most adults about this. If you ask them how many even numbers there are, they will usually say, "An infinite number," or they will say, "An unlimited number." If you ask them *how many*, they will probably say that you can't count them. But you can. There are $\aleph_0$ of them. You are going to have to wait a while before you learn about cardinal numbers larger than $\aleph_0$.

546. $4\,\dfrac{537}{600} \times 0 = 0$ Anything times zero is always equal to zero.

547. One-fourth of Joe's weight is fat. If he weighed 160 pounds, how much fat is he carrying around?

    One-fourth of 160 $4\overline{)160}$ (40)

    Joe is carrying around 40 pounds of fat. A gallon of water weighs about eight pounds. That means that his fat weighs him down as much as five jugs of water tied around his waist.

548. You can't write *IM* for 999 because *I* can only go in front of *V* or *X*. How would you write 999 in Roman numerals?

    CMXCIX   CM = 900   XC = 90   IX = 9

550. Joe had a nightmare that the price of jelly beans quadrupled. They were 29¢ each. How much would they be after the price increase?

They would cost four times as much.

$$\begin{array}{r} 29 \\ \times\ 4 \\ \hline 116 \end{array}$$

They would cost 116¢. (This could also be written as $1.16.)

552. Do $\frac{9}{12}$ and $\frac{75}{100}$ reduce to the same fraction?

Divide top and bottom of $\frac{9}{12}$ by 3 and we get $\frac{3}{4}$

Divide top and bottom by $\frac{75}{100}$ by 25 and we get $\frac{3}{4}$

Yes. They reduce to the same fraction.

554. Joe eats jelly beans by the handful. Over the years he has discovered that the best flavor balance is 4 fire red beans, 6 orange beans, and 7 vanilla beans. He puts these 17 beans in his hand, throws them into his mouth, chews hard, and swallows. The whole process takes 4 seconds.

How many handfuls could Joe eat in a minute?

In "real life" you don't encounter neat problems where every number that is given will be used in finding the answer. That only happens in some other math books. This book is more like real life.

In this problem we want to find out how many handfuls Joe could eat in an hour. It doesn't matter that some of the beans are fire red. It doesn't matter that Joe eats 17 beans in each handful.

What does matter is that eating a handful of beans takes 4 seconds. A minute is 60 seconds. How many handfuls (4 seconds) are in 60 seconds?

$$\begin{array}{r} 15 \\ 4\overline{)\,60} \end{array}$$ Joe can eat 15 handfuls in 60 seconds.

555. $4\,\frac{539}{600} + 0 = 4\,\frac{539}{600}$

When you add zero to any number, it leaves the number unchanged.

124

556. Suppose we have a number. Let's call it x. Suppose we know that x > 6.

        A) Could x be 3?

                That would mean that 3 > 6. That isn't true. Three isn't greater than 6.

        B) Could x be 4,754,984,681,613,005?

                Yes. It is true that 4,754,984,681,613,005 > 6. It is a *lot* bigger than 6.

        C) Could x be 6?

                No. It is not true that 6 is greater than 6. It is equal to 6.

558. Darlene hired a band to play at her birthday party. Each rabbit charged $8. How much would the four-rabbit band cost?

        The band would cost four times as much as each of the rabbits.

        $4 \times \$8 = \$32$

Darlene liked the price, but she was unaware that rabbits are not known as good singers. Or dancers. Or horn players.

560. 99×57

$$\begin{array}{r} 99 \\ \times\ 57 \\ \hline 693 \\ 495 \\ \hline 5643 \end{array}$$

563. Think of a number. Call that number y.

Suppose you know that y + 9 = 23. What is the value of y?

        y must be 14 since 14 + 9 = 23.

565. What are the chances that Joe will not propose before graduation?

        If there are two chances in ten that he will, then there are eight chances in ten that he won't. This means $\frac{8}{10}$ which reduces to $\frac{4}{5}$

567. If x < 4, then x might be 2 or 1 or 3 or 0 or 3½ or 2½. . . .

❀ Once you get to the next book (*Life of Fred: Decimals and Percents*) you will be able to say that x might be 3.5 or 2.7 or 0.98967 or 50% or 90%.

❀ Once you get to *Life of Fred: Beginning Algebra Expanded Edition*, you will be able to say that x might be $\sqrt{3}$ or π or –7.

❀ Once you get to *Life of Fred: Advanced Algebra Expanded Edition*, you will be able to say that x might be i^2 or a solution to $x^2 - 5x + 6 = 0$.

❀ Once you get to *Life of Fred: Trigonometry Expanded Edition*, you will be able to say that x might be sin 90°.

As you go on in mathematics, you will learn about all kinds of numbers.

There are numbers that are neither positive, negative, nor zero.

There are numbers that are bigger that any number in this list: 1, 2, 3, 4, 5, . . . and that list goes on forever. You often learn about those super big numbers when you take math as a junior in college. In elementary school, two kids sometimes play the Name the Largest Number game. The first kid might say 354,968,351,648,145,668,468. The second kid wins by saying 354,968,351,648,145,668,469, which is one larger than the first kid's number. It's a dumb game. The first kid always loses.

But if you play that game with someone who has studied higher math in college, he will say $\aleph_0$. This number is bigger than any number in this list: 1, 2, 3, 4, 5, 6, ... It is even bigger than 356135615135615155 49897498080841081801810811014586446846861611610161161611888 99941681235874683518451546841516841515618451883513517!

569. If Joe spent $\frac{31}{33}$ of his day thinking about fishing, what fraction of his day was left to think about other things?

He had $\frac{2}{33}$ left to think about other things. $\quad \frac{31}{33} + \frac{2}{33} = \frac{33}{33} = 1$

571. MCM is 1900 and XL is 40 so MCMXL = 1940

574. $4\frac{1}{4} \times 4\frac{1}{4} = \frac{17}{4} \times \frac{17}{4} = \frac{289}{16} = 16)\overline{289}^{\,18\ R1} = 18\frac{1}{16}$

577. Think of a number. Call that number x. Is it always true that x ≤ x?
    Yes. It is always true.
    Suppose the number you thought of was 3. Then x ≤ x would be
3 ≤ 3.
    ≤ means "less than or equal to." And certainly, 3 = 3. So 3 ≤ 3.

578. There are 24 hours in a day. Fred spends one-twelfth of each day
reading. How long is that?
    One-twelfth of 24
$$\begin{array}{r} 2 \\ 12\overline{)24} \end{array}$$
    Fred spends two hours each day reading.

580. 68×69

$$\begin{array}{r} 68 \\ \times\ 69 \\ \hline 612 \\ 408\ \ \\ \hline 4692 \end{array}$$

583. Change 200" into feet and inches.
To change inches into feet, you divide by 12.

$$\begin{array}{r} 16\ \ R\ 8 \\ 12\overline{)200} \\ -\ 12\ \ \ \\ \hline 80 \\ -\ 72 \\ \hline 8 \end{array}$$

    200" = 16' 8"

586. Darlene imagines that her wedding cake will weigh 296 pounds.
One-eighth of it will be frosting. How many pounds will the frosting
weigh?
    One-eighth of 296
$$\begin{array}{r} 37 \\ 8\overline{)296} \end{array}$$
    The frosting will weigh 37 pounds.

590. Darlene has a 3' × 8' rug in her bathroom.
Joe wanted to cut a circle out of that rug that was
as large as possible. How big could that circle be?

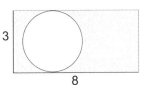

The circle would have a diameter of three feet.

591. Darlene spent her Saturday reading bridal magazines. (She leaves her college work until Sunday evening.) She started reading at 8 a.m. and finished at 3 p.m. She took a 17-minute break for lunch. How many minutes did she read?

From 8 a.m. to noon is 4 hours. From noon to 3 p.m. is 3 hours. From 8 a.m. to 3 p.m. is 7 hours. That's 420 minutes ($7 \times 60 = 420$).

Subtract 17 minutes from 420. She read for 403 minutes.

593. 287 inches is how many yards and inches? (36 inches = 1 yard)

$$\begin{array}{r} 7 \text{ R } 35 \\ 36\overline{)287} \\ -\ 252 \\ \hline 35 \end{array}$$

287 inches is 7 yards, 35 inches

595. 100 is "one hundred."

How would you say 4,000,000?   *Four million*

How would you say 40,000?   *Forty thousand*

How would you say 4,000,000,000? *Four billion*

598. Darlene had packed a zillion cherries for a picnic with Joe.

Joe said that he would be happy with $\frac{5}{8}$ of the cherries.

Darlene was on a diet and said she would be happy with $\frac{1}{3}$ of them. They both agreed that they could feed the rest of them to the duck.

The duck suggested that they get a bunch of plastic bags and divide the zillion cherries equally into the bags. How many bags should they use so that Joe could take $\frac{5}{8}$ of the bags and Darlene could take $\frac{1}{3}$ of the bags?

The smallest number of bags that will work is 24. Then if Joe took 15 bags, he would have $\frac{15}{24}$ of the cherries, which is $\frac{5}{8}$ of them.

If Darlene took 8 bags, she would have $\frac{8}{24}$ of the cherries which is $\frac{1}{3}$ of them.

600. mph means miles per hour.

128

601. Is 3 a cardinal number?

Yes. Cardinal numbers are numbers that can be used to count the number of members of a set.

This set {☎, ☺, ♣} has a cardinal number of 3.

This set { } has a cardinal number of zero.

603. Darlene, of course, invited Joe to her party. He brought along a bag of jelly beans in case there wasn't enough to eat at the party. It was a 15-pound bag and contained 3,708 jelly beans. (Joe had counted them.) The bag got heavy, and Joe set it down. The four rabbits thought it was a tip for their wonderful dancing, singing, and horn playing. They shared it equally among themselves. How many beans did each rabbit get?

$$\text{One-fourth of } 3{,}708 = \frac{1}{4} \times 3{,}708 = 4\overline{)3708} \;\; ^{927}$$

Each rabbit received 927 jelly beans.

605. Are brushing hair and putting on lipstick commutative?

You can do them in either order and get the same results. Those two operations are commutative.

607. How would you write in symbols *y is greater than or equal to 8*?

It would be written as $y \geq 8$.

Just for fun, note that this means the same as $8 \leq y$.

608. Which is larger: $\frac{2}{3}$ or $\frac{7}{10}$?

To compare fractions, the denominators must be alike.

$$\frac{2}{3} = \frac{20}{30} \qquad \frac{7}{10} = \frac{21}{30} \qquad \frac{2}{3} < \frac{7}{10} \qquad \frac{7}{10} \text{ is larger.}$$

610. Suppose we are looking a bunch of telephones. Is "older than" transitive?

Yes. If telephone A is older than telephone B, and telephone B is older than telephone C, then A must be older than C.

A

B

C

611. $\dfrac{4}{15} \times \dfrac{5}{8} = \dfrac{\cancel{4}^{1}}{\cancel{15}_{3}} \times \dfrac{\cancel{5}^{1}}{\cancel{8}_{2}} = \dfrac{1}{6}$

612. If my living room is $8\dfrac{1}{2}$ feet wide and $12\dfrac{3}{4}$ feet long, how many square feet of carpet will I need?

$$A = \ell w = 8\dfrac{1}{2} \times 12\dfrac{3}{4} = \dfrac{17}{2} \times \dfrac{51}{4} = \dfrac{867}{8}$$

$$\begin{array}{r} 108 \ \text{R} \ 3 \\ 8\overline{)867} \end{array}$$

I will need $108\dfrac{3}{8}$ square feet of carpet.

614.
$$2\dfrac{1}{6} = 2\dfrac{2}{12}$$
$$3\dfrac{1}{4} = 3\dfrac{3}{12}$$
$$3\dfrac{1}{2} = 3\dfrac{6}{12}$$
$$\dfrac{5}{6} = \dfrac{10}{12}$$
$$+ \ 3\dfrac{1}{3} = 3\dfrac{4}{12}$$

$$11\dfrac{25}{12} = 11 + 2\dfrac{1}{12} = 13\dfrac{1}{12} \ \text{miles}$$

615. What is the opposite rule for **taking half of something**?

That's easy. The opposite rule is to **double it**.

If I take half of 50, I get 25. If I double 25, I get 50, which is where I started.

617. Twenty-four hours at $17/hour is $\dfrac{24 \ \text{hours}}{1} \times \dfrac{\$17}{1 \ \text{hour}}$

$= \dfrac{24 \ \cancel{\text{hours}}}{1} \times \dfrac{\$17}{1 \ \cancel{\text{hour}}} = \$408.$

Did you know that when you multiply fractions you can also cancel hours?

Groom-Guard™

620. If there are 360° in a circle, how many degrees are in a quarter of a circle?

$\frac{1}{4}$ of 360°   4)$\overline{360}$ ... $\overset{90}{}$ There are 90° is a quarter of a circle.

621. It was a rectangle that measured $2\frac{1}{2}$ feet by $3\frac{1}{3}$ feet.

Its area equals $2\frac{1}{2} \times 3\frac{1}{3} = \frac{5}{2} \times \frac{10}{3} = \frac{5}{\cancel{2}_1} \times \frac{\cancel{10}^5}{3} = \frac{25}{3} = 8\frac{1}{3}$

The area of his desktop was $8\frac{1}{3}$ square feet.

623. Each of Joe's shirts had $12\frac{3}{4}$ grams of jelly bean drool on it.

(A gram is about the weight of a raisin.) What was the weight of the jelly bean drool on all seven shirts?

Seven shirts would have seven times as much drool as one shirt.

$7 \times 12\frac{3}{4} = \frac{7}{1} \times \frac{51}{4} = \frac{357}{4} = 4)\overline{357}\ \overset{89\ R1}{} = 89\frac{1}{4}$

The seven shirts had $89\frac{1}{4}$ grams of jelly bean drool.

624. Convert 8 years into months using a conversion factor.

Step 1: We know that 1 year = 12 months.
Step 2: The conversion factor will be either $\frac{1\ year}{12\ months}$ or $\frac{12\ months}{1\ year}$
Step 3: We start with $\frac{8\ years}{1}$

Step 4: We pick the conversion factor from step 2 so that the units cancel:

$\frac{8\ \cancel{years}}{1} \times \frac{12\ months}{1\ \cancel{year}} = 96\ months$

626. $\frac{3}{4}$ cup vanilla jelly beans plus $\frac{3}{4}$ cup cherry jelly beans plus

$\frac{3}{4}$ cup orange jelly beans $= \frac{3}{4} + \frac{3}{4} + \frac{3}{4} = \frac{9}{4}$ 4)$\overline{9}\ \overset{2\ R\ 1}{}$

Joe's recipe makes $2\frac{1}{4}$ cups.

630. Your list will probably be different than mine. Here are the onomatopoeic words I could think of: cackle, caw, cha-ching, chatter, cheep, chiming, chink, chirp, chomp, choo-choo, chortle, chuckle, chug, chump, chunk, clackety-clack, clang, clank, clap, clash, clatter, clickety-clack, clip clop, clobber, clop, clucking, clunk, cock-a-doodle-doo, cough, crack, crash, creak, cricket, crinkle, crisp, croak, croon, crow, crumple, crunchy, cry, cuckoo.

cheep!

633. If a circle had a radius of 89 meters, what would be its diameter?

A diameter is twice as long as a radius (in the same circle). The diameter would be 2×89.

$$\begin{array}{r} 89 \\ \times\ \ 2 \\ \hline 178 \end{array}$$

The diameter would be 178 meters.

635. The whole numbers = {0, 1, 2, 3, 4, . . . }. Joe needed the number 0 if he wanted to say how often he thought of Darlene each day.

His days were spent in deep thought about fishing and jelly beans.

636. What is the opposite rule for **divide by six**?

The opposite is multiply by six.

If, for example, I start with 24. If I divide by six, I get 4. Then if I multiply by six, I get 24, which was the number I started with.

Multiply by six is the inverse function to **divide by six**.

638. Joe bought eight anteaters. They dined on 448 ants and shared them equally. Anteaters are very nice. How many ants did each anteater get?

We divide 448 among 8 anteaters.

$$\begin{array}{r} 56 \\ 8{\overline{)448}} \\ -40 \\ \hline 48 \\ -48 \\ \hline 0 \end{array}$$

Each anteater enjoyed 56 ants.

639. What is the square root of 25?

      The square root of 25 is 5 because the square of 5 is 25.

      In algebra we use the symbol $\sqrt{}$ to indicate *take the square root of.* So $\sqrt{25} = 5$.

      And $\sqrt{100} = 10$. And $\sqrt{64} = 8$. And $\sqrt{1} = 1$.

640. 600 centimeters is how many meters? (100 centimeters = 1 meter)

$$\begin{array}{r} 6 \\ 100\overline{)\ 600} \\ -600 \\ \hline 0 \end{array}$$

      600 centimeters is 6 meters.

      A centimeter is a little less than half an inch. A meter is a little longer than a yard.

641. How long is 450" in feet and inches?

$$\begin{array}{r} 37 \text{ R } 6 \\ 12\overline{)\ 450} \end{array}$$

      The rope is 37 feet, 6 inches long.

642. Change into improper fractions:

$5\frac{2}{5} = \frac{27}{5}$ *5 times 5 . . . plus 2* $10\frac{3}{4} = \frac{43}{4}$ $2\frac{1}{16} = \frac{33}{16}$

644. $4\frac{1}{6} \times \frac{1}{15} = \frac{25}{6} \times \frac{1}{15} = \frac{\overset{5}{\cancel{25}}}{6} \times \frac{1}{\underset{3}{\cancel{15}}} = \frac{5}{18}$

645. In chemistry we know that one mole of carbon weighs 12 grams. How many moles are in 30 grams?

      Step 1: We know one mole = 12 grams of carbon.

      Step 2: The conversion factor will be either $\dfrac{\text{one mole}}{\text{12 grams}}$ or it will be $\dfrac{\text{12 grams}}{\text{one mole}}$

      Step 3: We are given 30 grams.

      Step 4: Pick the conversion factor so that the units cancel.

$$\frac{30 \text{ grams}}{1} \times \frac{\text{one mole}}{12 \text{ grams}} = \frac{\overset{5}{\cancel{30 \text{ grams}}}}{1} \times \frac{\text{one mole}}{\underset{2}{\cancel{12 \text{ grams}}}}$$

$$= \frac{5}{2} = 2\frac{1}{2} \text{ moles of carbon}$$

648. Change 314 minutes into hours and minutes. (Hint: To change minutes into hours you divide by 60. Any remainder will be leftover minutes.)

$$\begin{array}{r} 5 \quad\text{R } 14 \\ 60\overline{)314} \\ -\underline{300} \\ 14 \end{array}$$

314 minutes is 5 hours and 14 minutes.

649. Fred had a pan that was 14" × 30" and he wanted to make the largest pizza to fit in that pan. What will be the diameter of that pizza?

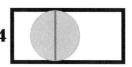

The largest pizza will have a 14-inch diameter.

650. Fred is shorter than Betty. Betty is shorter than Alexander. Must it be true that Fred is shorter than Alexander?

Yes. Suppose that x, y, and z are three numbers. Suppose you know that x < y and you know that y < z. Then it is always true that x < z. This is called the **transitive property of <**.

small essay
The Transitive Property

< has the transitive property. If x < y and y < z, then x < z.

= also has the transitive property. If x = y and y = z, then x must equal z.

Does "likes" have the transitive property? If Pat likes Chris and if Chris likes Morgan, must it be true that Pat likes Morgan? No. Pat might like Chris because they go out to pizza a lot. Chris might like Morgan because they enjoy hiking in the woods together. However, Pat might not like to do anything outdoors. "Likes" is not transitive.

end of small essay

652. 200 ounces is how many pounds. (16 ounces = 1 pound)

$$\begin{array}{r} 12 \text{ R } 8 \\ 16\overline{)\ 200} \\ -\ 16 \\ \hline 40 \\ -\ 32 \\ \hline 8 \end{array}$$

12 pounds, 8 ounces or

$12\,\dfrac{8}{16}$ which is 12½ pounds

653. One gross of eggs is how many dozen eggs?

How many 12's are in 144? Do we add, subtract, multiply, or divide? The way to figure that out is to take simpler numbers. *How many 2's are in 6?* That's easy. There are 3 twos in six. We divided.

To find out how many 12's are in 144, we divide.

There are twelve dozen in a gross.

$$\begin{array}{r} 12 \\ 12\overline{)144} \\ -\ 12 \\ \hline 24 \\ -\ 24 \\ \hline 0 \end{array}$$

655. A pound equals 16 ounces. If each fish ate $\dfrac{1}{8}$ of a pound of bait, how many ounces would that be?

$\dfrac{1}{8}$ of 16 means $16 \div 8$ means $8\overline{)16}^{\,2}$ Each fish ate 2 ounces.

656. Which of these have opposite actions?

A) Putting on a hat.

This has an opposite action. Take off the hat. You end up where you started: with no hat on your head.

B) Shutting your eyes.

This has an opposite action. Open your eyes.

C) Eating a slice of pizza.

How can you get back to that original slice of pizza? Throwing up won't work. This has no opposite action.

D) Opening a door.

Yes. Shut the door.

E) Adding 829 to a number.

The opposite action to adding 829 to a number is to subtract 829 from that number. Suppose you started with, say, 10. If you add 829 to 10, you get 839. Then if you subtract 829 from 839, you get back the original 10.

F) Multiplying by zero.

This has no opposite action. Suppose I start with some number—I'm not telling you what it is. Then I multiply by zero. The answer I get is zero. Can you tell me what my original number was? No, you can't.

658. The cake is one-eight frosting. If Joe ate all the frosting, what fraction of the cake would be left?

The whole cake is $\frac{8}{8}$

Joe eats $\frac{1}{8}$

That leaves $\frac{7}{8}$ $\qquad$ $\frac{8}{8} - \frac{1}{8} = \frac{7}{8}$

660. One of Darlene's magazines said that $\frac{1}{5}$ of your wedding budget should be for the wedding gown, $\frac{1}{3}$ for the wedding reception, and $\frac{1}{15}$ for photography. What fraction of the budget do these three items consume?

$$\frac{1}{5} + \frac{1}{3} + \frac{1}{15} = \frac{1 \times 3}{5 \times 3} + \frac{1 \times 5}{3 \times 5} + \frac{1}{15} = \frac{3}{15} + \frac{5}{15} + \frac{1}{15} = \frac{9}{15} = \frac{3}{5}$$

Three-fifths of the budget goes for gown, reception, and photos.

662. Is 15 an ordinal number? No. It is not an ordinal number.

Numbers like first, second, third, and fourth are ordinal numbers.

Numbers like 0, 1, and 15 are cardinal numbers. Cardinal numbers are used to count the members of a set. The cardinal number of {go fishing with him, cook for him, help him with homework, wear nail polish, shout at him} is 5.

The article "Fifteen Ways to Get Him to Notice You" gave Darlene ten more ideas.

663. Six of Darlene's bridal magazines weigh 5 pounds. She wants to pack 11 magazines on Joe's boat for their next fishing adventure. How much will the magazines weigh?

$$\frac{11 \text{ magazines}}{1} \times \frac{5 \text{ pounds}}{6 \text{ magazines}} = \frac{55}{6} = 9\frac{1}{6} \text{ pounds of magazines.}$$

664. Which number is smaller: 80 or 90?

80 is the smaller number. 80 < 90.

If the question had asked for the smaller *numeral*, then the answer would have been 90. Numerals are the written symbols. You can measure them by getting out a ruler and seeing how big they are.

665. Yes. If we draw it with a wet pen on a piece of paper

and then fold it diagonally

the original picture remains unchanged.

667. (continuing problem 649) What will be the radius of that pizza?

If the diameter is 14 inches, the radius will be 7 inches.

668. The tree was 12 feet tall. The ceiling in Joe's apartment is $8\frac{1}{3}$ feet tall. How much will Joe have to shorten his tree?

$$\begin{array}{r} 12 \\ -\ 8\frac{1}{3} \\ \hline \end{array} \qquad \begin{array}{r} 11\frac{3}{3} \\ -\ 8\frac{1}{3} \\ \hline 3\frac{2}{3} \end{array}$$

He will have to chop off $3\frac{2}{3}$ feet.

670. Joe's stamp was $6\frac{1}{8}$ inches wide and $7\frac{3}{4}$ inches long.

What was the area of Joe's stamp?

$$A = \ell w = 7\frac{3}{4} \times 6\frac{1}{8} = \frac{31}{4} \times \frac{49}{8} = \frac{1519}{32} \qquad 32\overline{)1519} \;\; ^{47\ R\ 15}$$

The area of Joe's stamp is $47\frac{15}{32}$ square inches.

671. How long is 450" in feet?

$$\begin{array}{r} 37 \text{ R } 6 \\ 12)\overline{\,450\,} \end{array}$$

The rope is $37\frac{6}{12} = 37\frac{1}{2}$ feet long.

673. $2\frac{7}{8}$ pounds of diamonds, $3\frac{2}{3}$ pounds of sapphires, $\frac{5}{6}$ pounds of emeralds, and $2\frac{3}{4}$ pounds of rhinestones.

How much did all of these jewels weigh?

$$2\frac{7}{8} = 2\frac{21}{24}$$
$$3\frac{2}{3} = 3\frac{16}{24}$$
$$\frac{5}{6} = \frac{20}{24}$$
$$2\frac{3}{4} = 2\frac{18}{24}$$

$$\begin{array}{r} 3 \text{ R } 3 \\ 24)\overline{\,75\,} \end{array}$$

$$+ \rule{4cm}{0.4pt}$$

$$7\frac{75}{24} = 7 + 3\frac{3}{24} = 10\frac{1}{8} \text{ pounds of jewels.}$$

This was no tiara (= coronet = small crown). This was a monster crown.

675. 83×26

$$\begin{array}{r} 83 \\ \times\, 26 \\ \hline 498 \\ 166 \\ \hline 2158 \end{array}$$

677. Darlene noticed that two-fifths of the $2\frac{7}{8}$ pounds of diamonds in her tiara were highly flawed. She said that they looked like they had bugs in them. How many pounds of flawed diamonds did she have?

Two-fifths of $2\frac{7}{8} = \frac{2}{5} \times 2\frac{7}{8} = \frac{2}{5} \times \frac{23}{8} = \frac{\overset{1}{\cancel{2}}}{5} \times \frac{23}{\underset{4}{\cancel{8}}} = \frac{23}{20}$

$= 1\frac{3}{20}$ pounds of flawed diamonds.

680. 100 is "one hundred."

How would you say 300,000,000?   *Three hundred million*

How would you say 47,000?   *Forty-seven thousand*

How would you say 97,000,000,000?   *Ninety-seven billion*

682. If it's 3000 miles away, how long will it take us if we go 27 miles per day?

$$27\overline{)3000}\quad\begin{array}{r}111\ R\ 3\\[-2pt]\end{array}$$

$$\begin{array}{r}-\ 27\\\hline 30\\-\ 27\\\hline 30\\-\ 27\\\hline 3\end{array}$$

$111\,\dfrac{3}{27}\ =\ 111\,\dfrac{1}{9}$ which is approximately 111 days

684. (continuing the problem #621) Joe decided to paint his desktop orange, which was his favorite color. The man at the paint store told Joe that it would cost $5\,\dfrac{1}{5}$ ¢ to paint each square foot. How much would it cost to paint his desktop?

In problem #621 we found that the area of his desktop was $8\,\dfrac{1}{3}$ square feet. $5\,\dfrac{1}{5}\ \times\ 8\,\dfrac{1}{3}\ =\ \dfrac{26}{5}\ \times\ \dfrac{25}{3}\ =\ \dfrac{26}{\cancel{5}_1}\ \times\ \dfrac{\cancel{25}^{5}}{3}\ =\ \dfrac{130}{3}\ =\ 43\,\dfrac{1}{3}$

It will cost $43\,\dfrac{1}{3}$ ¢ to paint his desktop orange.

685. After eating 37 pounds of frosting, Joe would weigh 185 pounds. What fraction of his body would be frosting?

37 is what part of 185? It is $\dfrac{37}{185}$

$\dfrac{37}{185}$ is a very hard fraction to reduce. Very hard. Few people would see that 37 divides evenly into 185.

If we divide top and bottom of $\dfrac{37}{185}$ by 37, we get $\dfrac{1}{5}$

One fifth of Joe would be frosting.

687. Change $\dfrac{706}{9}$ into a mixed number.

$$9\overline{)706}\quad\begin{array}{r}78\ R\ 4\\[-2pt]\end{array}\qquad\qquad\dfrac{706}{9}\ =\ 78\,\dfrac{4}{9}$$

139

689. If Fred bought a banana and put it in his desk drawer, it would spoil in 8 days.

If Fred bought a dozen bananas and put them in his desk drawer, how long would it take for all those bananas to spoil?

I hope you didn't multiply 8 × 12.

The second banana doesn't say to the first banana, "You spoil, and then I'll start spoiling." All twelve bananas start spoiling the minute Fred puts them in his desk. All of them would be spoiled in eight days.

691. Is this true: $\frac{5}{6} < \frac{7}{8}$?

To compare two fractions, we make the denominators alike.

$\frac{5}{6} = \frac{20}{24}$ $\frac{7}{8} = \frac{21}{24}$ It is true that $\frac{5}{6} < \frac{7}{8}$

693. There are 600 seats in the PieOne restaurant. If 400 of them are occupied, what *fraction* of the seats are empty?

There are 200 empty seats.   600 – 400 = 200

The fraction of empty seats is $\frac{200}{600}$ which reduces to $\frac{1}{3}$

695. $500 is what fraction of $650?

$\frac{500}{650} = \frac{50}{65} = \frac{10}{13}$ $500 is ten-thirteenths of $650.

697. We want to subtract $\frac{1}{2}$ pound from $3\frac{2}{3}$ pounds.

$3\frac{2}{3} = 3\frac{4}{6}$

$-\quad \frac{1}{2} = \frac{3}{6}$

$3\frac{1}{6}$ pounds of blue sapphires were left on her crown.

699. One square foot measures 12 inches by 12 inches. What is the area of a square foot in square inches?

A = ℓw = 12" × 12" = 144 square inches.

140

700. Which has the greatest number of Calories?

    A) Sixteen popsicles, each with 95 Calories   1,520 Calories

    B) Two ice cream sodas, each with 762 Calories   1,524 Calories

    C) Three small cherry pies, each with 513 Calories 1,539 Calories

Alternative C has the most Calories.

702. The kitchen floor was $10\frac{1}{4}$ feet by $16\frac{1}{2}$ feet. What was its area?

$$A = \ell w = 10\frac{1}{4} \times 16\frac{1}{2} = \frac{41}{4} \times \frac{33}{2} = \frac{1353}{8}$$

$$8)\overline{1353} \quad \frac{169 \text{ R } 1}{}$$

The area of the kitchen floor is $169\frac{1}{8}$ square feet.

704. I can count four different lines of symmetry: one horizontal, one vertical, and two diagonals.

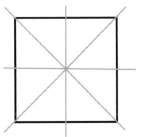

705. If 3,500 Calories translates into one pound of fat on your tummy, what would 4,000 Calories equal in terms of fat?

    Step 1: We know 3,500 Calories = 1 pound of fat.

    Step 2: The conversion factor will be either $\frac{3500 \text{ Calories}}{1 \text{ lb. of fat}}$

or it will be $\frac{1 \text{ lb. of fat}}{3500 \text{ Calories}}$

    Step 3: We are given 4,000 Calories.

    Step 4: Use the conversion factor that makes the units cancel.

$$\frac{4000 \text{ Calories}}{1} \times \frac{1 \text{ lb. of fat}}{3500 \text{ Calories}}$$

$$= \frac{\overset{8}{\cancel{4000}} \text{ Calories}}{1} \times \frac{1 \text{ lb. of fat}}{\underset{7}{\cancel{3500}} \text{ Calories}} = \frac{8}{7} = 1\frac{1}{7} \text{ pounds of fat}$$

706. Four and a half times $200 $= 4\frac{1}{2} \times 200$

$$= \frac{9}{2} \times \frac{200}{1} = \frac{9}{\underset{1}{\cancel{2}}} \times \frac{\overset{100}{\cancel{200}}}{1} = \frac{900}{1} = \$900 \text{ for flawless diamonds}$$

707. What is the opposite to **add 3 and then multiply by 10**?

You first divide by 10 and then subtract 3.

For example, suppose you start with the number 5. If you add 3 and then multiply by 10, you get 80.

To get back to 5, you first divide by 10 and then subtract 3.

708. Each shirt had $3\frac{1}{2}$ grams of ketchup, $2\frac{1}{8}$ grams of Sluice, and $12\frac{3}{4}$ grams of jelly bean drool on it. What was the weight of all that mess on each shirt?

$$3\frac{1}{2} = 3\frac{4}{8}$$
$$2\frac{1}{8} = 2\frac{1}{8}$$
$$+ \quad 12\frac{3}{4} = 12\frac{6}{8}$$

$$17\frac{11}{8} = 17 + 1\frac{3}{8} = 18\frac{3}{8} \text{ grams of mess on a shirt}$$

710. It takes Joe 26 minutes to dig up a pound of worms. How long would it take him to dig up 11 pounds?

It would take him eleven times as long. It would take him 26×11.

$$
\begin{array}{r}
26 \\
\times\ 11 \\
\hline
26 \\
26 \\
\hline
286
\end{array}
$$

It would take him 286 minutes.

712. I have $273\frac{3}{8}$ pounds of stuff I can toss in the garbage. If everything I own weighs $328\frac{3}{4}$ pounds, how much will I have left after the marriage?

$$328\frac{3}{4} = 328\frac{6}{8}$$
$$- \quad 273\frac{3}{8} = 273\frac{3}{8}$$

$$55\frac{3}{8} \text{ pounds she will have left after the wedding.}$$

714. When Joe is attending one of Fred's 60-minute lectures, he spends three-tenths of the time doodling on his binder paper. How many minutes is that?

$$\text{Three-tenths of 60 minutes} = \frac{3}{10} \times \frac{60}{1} = \frac{180}{10} = 18 \text{ minutes}$$

715. Darlene's empty purse weighs $4\frac{1}{4}$ pounds. She packs it with $5\frac{1}{2}$ pounds of nail polish, $9\frac{1}{6}$ pounds of magazines, and $1\frac{1}{8}$ pounds of lipstick. How much will all that weigh?

$$4\frac{1}{4} = 4\frac{6}{24}$$

$$5\frac{1}{2} = 5\frac{12}{24}$$

$$9\frac{1}{6} = 9\frac{4}{24}$$

$$+\quad 1\frac{1}{8} = 1\frac{3}{24}$$

$$\overline{\qquad\qquad\qquad}$$

$$19\frac{25}{24} = 19 + 1\frac{1}{24} = 20\frac{1}{24} \text{ pounds}$$

717. Joe's desktop is $8\frac{1}{3}$ square feet. How many square inches is that?

Since 1 square foot equals 144 square inches, $8\frac{1}{3}$ square feet will equal $8\frac{1}{3} \times 144 = \frac{25}{3} \times \frac{144}{1} = \frac{3600}{3} = 1,200$ square inches.

720. If Joe could eat a 2-pound bag of jelly beans in 6 minutes, why would it be silly to say he could eat twelve 2-pound bags of jelly beans in 72 minutes?

Everyone knows that one jelly bean will fill Fred up. It would be days before he could eat a second jelly bean.

Joe is different. He could eat two or three bags of jelly beans at the rate of one bag per six minutes. But even Joe starts to get full after eating four or six pounds of jelly beans. By the time he has eaten ten pounds of jelly beans (that's five bags), he is getting stuffed. His speed really starts to slow down. After 14 pounds, he starts to get sick.

It would probably take Joe a couple of days to consume a dozen 2-pound bags (24 pounds!) of jelly beans.

721. When Darlene is on the boat while Joe is fishing, he has her clean the fish that he's caught. She can clean 5 fish in 8 minutes. Using a conversion factor find out how long it would take her to clean 30 fish.]

Step 1: We know that 5 fish = 8 minutes.

Step 2: Either $\dfrac{5\text{ fish}}{8\text{ minutes}}$ or $\dfrac{8\text{ minutes}}{5\text{ fish}}$

Step 3: We start with 30 fish. That's $\dfrac{30\text{ fish}}{1}$

Step 4: We pick the conversion factor from step 2 so that the units cancel: $\dfrac{\overset{6}{\cancel{30\text{ fish}}}}{1} \times \dfrac{8\text{ minutes}}{\underset{1}{\cancel{5\text{ fish}}}} = 48$ minutes

723. The door to Fred's office is 78" tall. Since Fred is only 36" tall, he never hits his head on the top of the doorframe. He is thinking of getting a really tall hat. What is the tallest hat he could get and not have to duck when walking into his office?

The difference between 78 and 36 is

$$\begin{array}{r} 78 \\ -\ 36 \\ \hline 42 \end{array}$$

He could get a 42" tall hat.

725. Darlene had planned an 84-day honeymoon with Joe. If Joe ate 37 pounds of frosting, he would spend one-twelfth of those 84 honeymoon days in the hospital. How many days of their honeymoon would be lost?

One-twelfth of 84 is $\dfrac{1}{12} \times 84$ which is $12\overline{)84}\,^7$

Seven days of their honeymoon would be lost.

727. At KITTENS University the teachers' monthly salaries total $83,938. The president's salary is $197,668. The janitors' salaries total $3,077. What is the total monthly salaries for all these people?

$$\begin{array}{r} 83{,}938 \\ 197{,}668 \\ +\ \ \ 3{,}077 \\ \hline 284{,}683 \end{array}$$

The total is $284,683.

730. If Joe were four times stronger, he could lift 60 kg with his left arm. How much could Joe lift with his left arm?

One-fourth of 60 $= 4\overline{)60}^{\,15}$ Joe could lift 15 kg with his left arm. (Kilograms are a measurement in the metric system. Pounds are a measure in the imperial system. A kilogram is a little more than two pounds.)

733. If Fred rode in a car on the freeway, he could go 65 mph.

If Fred tried to drive a car, his speed would be 0 mph. His legs are too short to reach the gas pedal.

Fred could go much faster than 65 mph if he were in an airplane.

He could go faster than an airplane if he were in a rocket ship.

What can go faster than a rocket ship? The answer is *your imagination*. You could be standing on the campus of KITTENS University in Kansas where Fred teaches. You could imagine that you were at Disneyland in California, wearing a coonskin cap and paddling in the waters of Adventureland. You went from Kansas to California faster than any rocket ship could go.

735. Joe was given this problem: **Suppose x is cardinal number and suppose that 40 < x < 42. What is x?**

Joe wanted to be fancy and wrote $40\,\frac{7}{8}$

The teacher said his answer was wrong. Why?

The question said that x was a *cardinal number*. Cardinal numbers are the counting numbers. They are the numbers like 0 or 1 or 2 or 3 or 4 or 5 or 6, etc.

The number $40\,\frac{7}{8}$ is not a counting number. You can't have $40\,\frac{7}{8}$ flavors of ice cream. You can't have $40\,\frac{7}{8}$ cars.

737. Change 286 minutes into hours and minutes.

$$\begin{array}{r} 4 \ \ R \ \ 46 \\ 60\overline{)286} \\ -\,240 \\ \hline 46 \end{array}$$

The 286 minutes that Joe spent digging up worms is 4 hours, 46 minutes.

145

738. If five-eighths of the customers at PieOne are math majors, what fraction of the customers are not math majors?

$$1 - \frac{5}{8} = \frac{8}{8} - \frac{5}{8} = \frac{3}{8}$$

Three-eights of the customers are not math majors.

small essay

Was This Drawing Really Fair?

Is it possible to be happy and not be a math major? Is the world really divided into math majors and sad people?

Of course not. That would be silly.

At most universities you have to be a third-year student (a junior) in order to declare your major. During the first two years (freshman and sophomore) you are required to take courses in many different areas. You might be studying German, art history, literature, calculus, astronomy, or chemistry. This is to give you time to decide that you really like math better than the other stuff.

There are lots of people who are not sad and who are not math majors. They are freshman and sophomores!

end of small essay

740. If the diameter of a circle is 740, what would be its radius?

A radius is one-half as long as a diameter.

$$740 \div 2 \qquad \begin{array}{r} 370 \\ 2\overline{)740} \\ -\underline{6} \\ 14 \\ -\underline{14} \\ 0 \end{array}$$

The radius would be 370.

742. Three days is what fraction of a week?

Three days is $\frac{3}{7}$ of a week.

744. Six dollars is what fraction of $870?

$\frac{6}{870}$ This can be reduced. If we divide top and bottom by 2 we get $\frac{3}{435}$ This can be reduced. Dividing top and bottom by 3, we get $\frac{1}{145}$

Joe's plastic flower is $\frac{1}{145}$ of the flower budget.

745. (continuing #702) Joe figured that the first thing he should do is wax the kitchen floor. He estimated that it would take 8 seconds to do each square foot. How long would it take for him to do the whole floor?

In the previous problem we found that the kitchen floor was $169\frac{1}{8}$ square feet.

$$\frac{169 \frac{1}{8} \text{ square feet}}{1} \times \frac{8 \text{ seconds}}{1 \text{ square foot}}$$

$$= 169\frac{1}{8} \times 8 \text{ seconds}$$

$$= \frac{1353}{8} \times \frac{8}{1} = 1{,}353 \text{ seconds} \qquad 60)\overline{1353} \quad 22 \text{ R } 33$$

$$= 22 \text{ minutes, 33 seconds.}$$

747. $\frac{1}{6} + \frac{1}{8} = \frac{4}{24} + \frac{3}{24} = \frac{7}{24}$

750. $\frac{8}{15} - \frac{2}{15} = \frac{6}{15}$ which reduces to $\frac{2}{5}$

753. $\frac{5}{6} \times \frac{2}{15} \times \frac{9}{13} = \frac{5}{6} \times \frac{2}{15} \times \frac{9}{13} = \frac{1}{3} \times \frac{1}{3} \times \frac{9}{13} =$

$\frac{1}{3} \times \frac{1}{3} \times \frac{9}{13} = \frac{1}{13}$

You may have canceled in a different order. You will still get the same answer.

755. A circle with a diameter of $8\frac{1}{4}$ inches.

The circumference C = $3\frac{1}{7} \times$ diameter $= 3\frac{1}{7} \times 8\frac{1}{4}$

$= \dfrac{22}{7} \times \dfrac{33}{4} = \dfrac{\overset{11}{\cancel{22}}}{7} \times \dfrac{33}{\underset{2}{\cancel{4}}} = \dfrac{363}{14} = 14\overline{)363}\;^{25\ R\ 13}$

$= 25\frac{13}{14}$ inches is the circumference of the ketchup circle.

757. Which of these is easier to do? A) $\dfrac{7}{9} + \dfrac{1}{8}$ or B) $\dfrac{7}{9} \times \dfrac{1}{8}$

Multiplying fractions is usually much easier than add them.

For example, $\dfrac{7}{9} + \dfrac{1}{8} = \dfrac{56}{72} + \dfrac{9}{72} = \dfrac{65}{72}$

$\dfrac{7}{9} \times \dfrac{1}{8} = \dfrac{7}{72}$

758. It costs $\dfrac{4}{11}$ ¢ per hair and the bill was 4,000¢.

How many $\dfrac{4}{11}$'s are there in 4000?

$4000 \div \dfrac{4}{11} = \dfrac{4000}{1} \times \dfrac{11}{4} = \dfrac{\overset{1000}{\cancel{4000}}}{1} \times \dfrac{11}{\underset{1}{\cancel{4}}} = 11,000$ hairs.

759. What is the square of $5\frac{1}{3}$?

The square of $5\frac{1}{3}$ is $5\frac{1}{3} \times 5\frac{1}{3}$

$= \dfrac{16}{3} \times \dfrac{16}{3} = \dfrac{256}{9} = 9\overline{)256}\;^{28\ R\ 4} = 28\frac{4}{9}$

760. $8\frac{1}{3} - 4\frac{2}{3}$

$\begin{aligned} 8\frac{1}{3} &= 7\frac{3}{3} + \frac{1}{3} = 7\frac{4}{3} \\ -\ 4\frac{2}{3} &= 4\frac{2}{3} \qquad\quad = 4\frac{2}{3} \\ \hline & \qquad\qquad\qquad\quad\ \ 3\frac{2}{3} \end{aligned}$

761. $\dfrac{4}{5} \div \dfrac{8}{9} = \dfrac{4}{5} \times \dfrac{9}{8} = \dfrac{\overset{1}{\cancel{4}}}{5} \times \dfrac{9}{\underset{2}{\cancel{8}}} = \dfrac{9}{10}$

762. Darlene had spent $40. Her total budget for her hair for the whole year was $200. What fraction of her hair budget was wasted on getting her hair painted?

This asks, "$40 is what fraction of $200?"

$\frac{40}{200}$ and this reduces to $\frac{1}{5}$ (when you divide top and bottom by 40).

777. Here is a rough copy of the check with the three blanks filled in.

date _March 27, 2016_

Pay to the order of _____Cancer Reseach_____ $ _5,440⁰⁰_

Five thousand, four hundred forty and 00/100 dollars

Two things to notice about check writing:

(1) You don't write $5,440.00 because that is too easy to change into $5,440,000.00. You just turn the period into a comma and add more zeros. (There are bad people out there in the world that might do that.) Instead you put the cents higher and underlined. Here's how you would write seven dollars and 26 cents: $7²⁶

(2) On the line where you write out the number, it becomes _Seven and 26/100_ dollars.

780. Is it possible to draw a triangle with two right angles?

I can't think of how to do that. When I try, I get something like this ☞ and that's not a triangle.

781. Alexander is 73" tall. How much is that in feet and inches? (To change inches into feet you divide by 12.)

$$\begin{array}{r} 6 \ \ R\,1 \\ 12\overline{)\,73} \\ -\,72 \\ \hline 1 \end{array}$$

Alexander is 6' 1" tall.

149

783. One-fifth of 3 fish means 3 fish divided equally into 5 parts.
His milkshake mug held $\frac{3}{5}$ of a fish.

784.

$$12\frac{3}{4} \;=\; 12\frac{6}{8} \;=\; 11\frac{8}{8}+\frac{6}{8} \;=\; 11\frac{14}{8}$$

$$-\quad 2\frac{7}{8} \qquad\qquad\qquad\qquad =\quad 2\frac{7}{8}$$

$$9\frac{7}{8}$$

The waters would have to rise $9\frac{7}{8}$ feet before they reached the bottom of the building.

786. Darlene normally spends $29 each month for nail polish. One month the price of nail polish went up and she had to spend $47 instead. How much more money did she have to spend that month on nail polish?

The price went from $29 to $47. The difference is $47 - 29$.

$$\begin{array}{r} 47 \\ -\ 29 \\ \hline 18 \end{array}$$

She had to spend $18 more that month.

788. She reads 4 magazine pages for every 7 fish she cleans. How many pages will she read while cleaning 30 fish? Use a conversion factor.

Step 1: We know that 4 magazine pages = 7 fish.

Step 2: Either $\dfrac{4 \text{ pages}}{7 \text{ fish}}$ or $\dfrac{7 \text{ fish}}{4 \text{ pages}}$

Step 3: We are given 30 fish. That means $\dfrac{30 \text{ fish}}{1}$

Step 4: Pick the conversion factor from step 2 so that the units cancel: $\dfrac{30 \text{ fish}}{1} \times \dfrac{4 \text{ pages}}{7 \text{ fish}} = \dfrac{120 \text{ pages}}{7} = 7\overline{)120}\ \ ^{17\ R\ 1}$

She will read $17\frac{1}{7}$ magazine pages while cleaning 30 fish.

789. A pentagon is a figure with five sides. How many vertices does it have?

If it's got five sides, it has to have five vertices.

790. 100 is "one hundred."

How would you say 243?   *Two hundred forty-three*
You don't say "and"

How would you say 45,000,000,000?   *Forty-five billion*

How would you say 237,000,000?   *Two hundred thirty-seven million*
You don't say "and"

792. The ketchup.

794. If Joe had 4,775 jelly beans, how many more would he need to have a million jelly beans?

$$
\begin{array}{r}
1,000,000 \\
-\quad\;\; 4,775 \\
\hline
995,225
\end{array}
$$

He would need 995,225 more jelly beans.

796. What is the least common multiple (LCM) of 5, 25, and 100?

The smallest number that 5, 25, and 100 divide evenly into is 100.

798. Joe's Special Jelly Bean Worms™ = 7 licorice (black) jelly beans make one worm. How many jelly beans would it take to make 500 worms?

It would take 500 times as much as a single worm.

$$
\begin{array}{r}
500 \\
\times \quad 7 \\
\hline
3500
\end{array}
$$

It would take 3,500 jelly beans to make 500 worms.

800. 72×58

$$
\begin{array}{r}
72 \\
\times\; 58 \\
\hline
576 \\
360 \\
\hline
4176
\end{array}
$$

802. $932 \times 31 \times 55819 \times 0 = ?$

Zero times anything is equal to zero.

804. Fifty feet of fishing line cost $3. Using a conversion factor, find out how much 75 feet would cost.

Step 1: We know that 50 feet = $3.

Step 2: The conversion factor will be either $\dfrac{50 \text{ feet}}{\$3}$ or $\dfrac{\$3}{50 \text{ feet}}$

Step 3: We are given 75 feet.

Step 4: We pick the conversion factor from step 2 so that the units will cancel.

$$\frac{75 \text{ feet}}{1} \times \frac{\$3}{50 \text{ feet}} = \frac{\overset{3}{\cancel{75 \text{ feet}}}}{1} \times \frac{\$3}{\underset{2}{\cancel{50 \text{ feet}}}} = \frac{\$9}{2}$$

= four and a half dollars.

806. A jelly bean storage building can hold 2 tons of jelly beans. Currently, Joe has one-sixteenth of a ton of jelly beans. How much more jelly beans would Joe need in order to fill that building?

$$2 \qquad = 1\frac{16}{16}$$
$$- \qquad \frac{1}{16} = \frac{1}{16}$$
$$\rule{3cm}{0.4pt}$$
$$1\frac{15}{16}$$

He would need $1\frac{15}{16}$ tons more.

808. Joe thought for a moment and said, "I'd like $\frac{2}{5}$ of that pizza and you could have $\frac{1}{5}$ of it." How much of the pizza would they have?

In other words, what does $\frac{2}{5} + \frac{1}{5}$ equal? $\frac{2}{5} + \frac{1}{5} = \frac{3}{5}$

This is going to be a lot of pizza for the two of them. Darlene was planning on having 300 people at their wedding. The wedding cake she was dreaming of might weigh 396 pounds. If Joe had two-fifths of a 396-pound pizza, he wouldn't have much room left for jelly beans.

810. What is the square root of 64?

$\sqrt{64} = 8$ because $8 \times 8 = 64$.

152

812. Joe had $2\frac{1}{2}$ ounce packages of worms for fishing. How many of those packages would he need if he wanted $17\frac{1}{2}$ ounces of worms?

We are looking for how many $2\frac{1}{2}$ ounce packages are in $17\frac{1}{2}$ ounces.

$$17\frac{1}{2} \div 2\frac{1}{2} = \frac{35}{2} \div \frac{5}{2} = \frac{35}{2} \times \frac{2}{5} = \frac{\cancel{35}^{7}}{\cancel{2}_{1}} \times \frac{\cancel{2}^{1}}{\cancel{5}_{1}} = 7$$

Seven of the $2\frac{1}{2}$ ounce packages are needed.

813. Pat was able to clean 100 hairs in $2\frac{1}{2}$ minutes. How long will it take Pat to clean up the 11,000 hairs on Darlene's head?

Step 1: We know that 100 hairs $= 2\frac{1}{2}$ minutes.

Step 2: The conversion factor will be either $\dfrac{100 \text{ hairs}}{2\frac{1}{2} \text{ minutes}}$ or it will be $\dfrac{2\frac{1}{2} \text{ minutes}}{100 \text{ hairs}}$

Step 3: We are given 11,000 hairs, which we want to convert into minutes.

Step 4: We pick the conversion factor so that the units cancel.

$$\frac{\cancel{11,000 \text{ hairs}}^{110}}{1} \times \frac{2\frac{1}{2} \text{ minutes}}{\cancel{100 \text{ hairs}}_{1}} = 110 \times 2\frac{1}{2} = \frac{\cancel{110}^{55}}{1} \times \frac{5}{\cancel{2}_{1}}$$

$= 275$ minutes

816.

Joe liked this because it reminded him of a compass that Darlene had bought for him so that he wouldn't get lost when fishing on the Great Lake near KITTENS University.

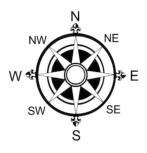

818. Think of a number. Call that number x. Could it ever be true that $x = x + 3$?

It is never true.

Suppose the number you thought of was 5. Then $x = x + 3$ would mean $5 = 8$. This isn't true.

Suppose the number you thought of was 26. Then $x = x + 3$ would mean $26 = 29$. This isn't true.

820. Which of these are true and which are false?

$8 < 5$ False. It is true that $5 < 8$.

$100 < 101$ True.

$30\frac{1}{2} < 40$ True. $30\frac{1}{2}$ is less than 31, and 31 is less than 40.

822. $\frac{1}{5} \times \frac{3}{8} \times \frac{13}{33} \times \frac{0}{15} = ?$

The last fraction is equal to zero (by General Rule #2).

Multiplying by zero always gives an answer of zero.

$$\frac{1}{5} \times \frac{3}{8} \times \frac{13}{33} \times \frac{0}{15} = 0$$

823. Divide MMDCXIX by XXVII and express your answer in Roman numerals.

$$27\overline{)2619}^{\;97}$$

MMDCXIX ÷ XXVII = XCVII

824. Are the operations of *square a number* and *add 3* commutative?

That is the same as asking whether

A) squaring a number and then adding 3 will always give you the same answer as

B) adding 3 and then squaring.

Those two operations are not commutative. In fact, they will rarely give you the same answer.

For example, start with the number 4. If I square it and then add 3 I get 19. If I start with 4 and add 3 and then square it, I get 49.

825. Then he did $\dfrac{7}{9} + \dfrac{11}{14} = \dfrac{\overset{1}{\cancel{7}}}{9} + \dfrac{11}{\underset{2}{\cancel{14}}} = \dfrac{11}{18}$

This is a mistake. You can only cancel when you are **multiplying** fractions.

When you are adding fractions, you need to find the least common denominator (LCD).

$$\frac{7}{9} + \frac{11}{14} = \frac{7 \times 14}{9 \times 14} + \frac{11 \times 9}{14 \times 9} = \frac{98}{126} + \frac{99}{126} = \frac{197}{126} = 1\frac{71}{126}$$

Adding fractions is often harder than multiplying fractions.

828. One sixteenth of a ton is how many pounds?

Using a conversion factor,

$$\frac{1/16 \text{ ton}}{1} \times \frac{2000 \text{ lbs.}}{1 \text{ ton}} = \frac{1/16 \text{ ton}}{1} \times \frac{2000 \text{ lbs.}}{1 \text{ ton}} =$$

$$= \frac{1}{16} \times \frac{2000 \text{ lbs.}}{1} = \overset{\displaystyle 125}{16\overline{)2000}}$$

Joe currently has 125 lbs. of jelly beans.

830. **CURIE'S GLOW-IN-THE-LIGHT NAIL POLISH**™ costs \$5 for a $\dfrac{1}{6}$ ounce bottle. Darlene needs 4 ounces. (She is doing both finger and toe nails and is putting in several coats.) How many bottles does she need?

We want to know how many $\dfrac{1}{6}$'s are in 4.

$$4 \div \frac{1}{6} = \frac{4}{1} \div \frac{1}{6} = \frac{4}{1} \times \frac{6}{1} = 24 \text{ bottles are needed.}$$

In Real Life, the problems you face will not always include *only* the numbers that you will use in solving the problem. In this problem, you were told that a bottle cost \$5.

Some students who have learned their math from *Math Books for the Subnormally Intelligent* will want to use the \$5 somehow in doing the problem. That's because the problems in those books only include the necessary numbers. That is poor preparation for living in the Real World.

831. If I have a quadrilateral in which the opposite sides are parallel, must it be a rectangle?

No. It might look like this ☞

834. With 5 strokes of the comb he could knock off 34 scales. How many strokes would it take knock off *at least* 380 scales.

Step 1: We know that 5 strokes = 34 scales.

Step 2: The conversion factor will be either $\dfrac{5 \text{ strokes}}{34 \text{ scales}}$ or it will be $\dfrac{34 \text{ scales}}{5 \text{ strokes}}$

Step 3: We want at least 380 scales.

Step 4: Pick the conversion factor so that the units cancel.

$$\frac{380 \text{ scales}}{1} \times \frac{5 \text{ strokes}}{34 \text{ scales}} = \frac{380 \text{ scales}}{1} \times \frac{5 \text{ strokes}}{34 \text{ scales}} =$$

$$= \frac{1900 \text{ strokes}}{34} = 34\overline{)1900}^{\,55 \text{ R } 30}$$

To clean 380 scales will take $55\frac{30}{34}$ strokes.

Since you can't make a part of a stoke, it will take 56 strokes to knock off *at least* 380 scales.

835. Darlene had 99 cans of hair spray. If she used one can each week, roughly how long will those 99 cans last?

My calculation: There are roughly 100 cans. That will last 100 weeks since she uses one can each week.

There are roughly 50 weeks in a year. So the cans should last about two years.   B) 2 years

836. What is a rough estimate of $4\frac{1}{4} + 5\frac{1}{2} + 9\frac{1}{6} + 1\frac{1}{8}$

My calculation: Adding up the $4 + 5 + 9 + 1$, I get 19. I toss in another 1 for the $\frac{1}{4} + \frac{1}{2} + \frac{1}{6} + \frac{1}{8}$ That gives me a total of 20.

866. Change 78" into feet and inches. (Hint: Divide by 12 and any remainder will be the inches left over.)

$$\begin{array}{r} 6\ \ \text{R}\ 6 \\ 12\overline{)78} \\ -72 \\ \hline 6 \end{array}$$

78" equals 6' 6".

867. $\dfrac{2\frac{1}{8}}{5\frac{2}{3}} = 2\frac{1}{8} \div 5\frac{2}{3} = \dfrac{17}{8} \div \dfrac{17}{3} = \dfrac{17}{8} \times \dfrac{3}{17} = \dfrac{3}{8}$

868. Joe could never figure out why Darlene was so happy to clean the fish he caught. (He had never read the articles in the bridal magazines.) In order to make Darlene happier, he invented new system of catching fish. For every 5 fish he caught under the old system, he could catch 8 under the new system. If he caught 20 under the old system, he many could he catch under the new system. Use a conversion factor.

Step 1: We know that 5 fish under old system = 8 under new system

Step 2: Either $\dfrac{5 \text{ fish old system}}{8 \text{ fish new system}}$ or $\dfrac{8 \text{ fish new system}}{5 \text{ fish old system}}$

Step 3: We know 20 fish old system.

Step 4: Pick the conversion factor from step 2 so that the units cancel.

$$\dfrac{20 \text{ fish old system}}{1} \times \dfrac{8 \text{ fish new system}}{5 \text{ fish old system}}$$

$$= \dfrac{\overset{4}{\cancel{20 \text{ fish old system}}}}{1} \times \dfrac{8 \text{ fish new system}}{\underset{1}{\cancel{5 \text{ fish old system}}}}$$

$= 32$ fish will be caught in the new system

869. If each can of hair spray costs $4, roughly how much did the 99 cans cost?

My calculation: One hundred cans at $4 each would cost $400. So 99 cans would cost roughly C) $400.

870. Is it possible to name a number—let's call it x—so that $5 < x < 3$?

I can't think of any number that is both larger than 5 and also less than 3. That would be like finding someone is who is more than five feet tall and also less than three feet tall.

Even when you get to algebra, trig, or calculus, we will never be able to find a value for x so that $5 < x < 3$.

872. Change $10\frac{3}{4}$ into an improper fraction.

Four times 10 . . . plus 3 turns $10\frac{3}{4}$ into $\frac{43}{4}$

874. Each of Joe's shirts had $12\frac{3}{4}$ grams of jelly bean drool on it. A gram of jelly bean drool is equal to $3\frac{4}{51}$ Calories. If the ants ate the jelly bean drool off of one of his shirts, how many Calories would they receive?

Step 1: We know 1 gram = $3\frac{4}{51}$ Calories.

Step 2: The conversion factor will be either $\dfrac{1 \text{ gram}}{3\ 4/51 \text{ Calories}}$ or $\dfrac{3\ 4/51 \text{ Calories}}{1 \text{ gram}}$

Step 3: We are given $12\frac{3}{4}$ grams.

Step 4: We pick the conversion factor so that the units will cancel.

$$\frac{12\ 3/4 \text{ grams}}{1} \times \frac{3\ 4/51 \text{ Calories}}{1 \text{ gram}} =$$

$$= 12\frac{3}{4} \times 3\frac{4}{51} \text{ Calories} = \frac{51}{4} \times \frac{157}{51} = \frac{51}{4} \times \frac{157}{51}$$

$$= \frac{157}{4} = 4\overline{)157}\ ^{39\ R\ 1} = 39\frac{1}{4} \text{ Calories}$$

875. Darlene applied six coats of **CURIE'S GLOW-IN-THE-LIGHT NAIL POLISH** to her finger nails. Her hands were now 13 pounds heavier than before she put on the six coats.

Roughly, how much did each coat weigh?

My calculation: If her hands were 12 pounds heavier, then each of the six coats would weigh 2 pounds (since $6 \times 2 = 12$).   C) 2 pounds

876. When Joe goes out fishing, there is three-fourths of a chance that he will injure himself. One spring he went fishing for 80 days. How many days during that spring did he injure himself?

(Hint: This is the same as asking $\frac{3}{4} = \frac{?}{80}$)

$$\frac{3 \times 20}{4 \times 20} = \frac{60}{80} \qquad \text{He injured himself on 60 days.}$$

878. Each bottle would put out $3\frac{3}{4}$ lumens of light. How many bottles will Darlene need to get 615 lumens of light?

How many $3\frac{3}{4}$'s are in 615?

$$615 \div 3\frac{3}{4} = \frac{615}{1} \div \frac{15}{4} = \frac{615}{1} \times \frac{4}{15} = \frac{\overset{41}{\cancel{615}}}{1} \times \frac{4}{\cancel{15}} = 164 \text{ bottles}$$

880. The kitchen floor was $10\frac{1}{4}$ feet by $16\frac{1}{2}$ feet.

The perimeter is $10\frac{1}{4} + 16\frac{1}{2} + 10\frac{1}{4} + 16\frac{1}{2}$

$$= 10\frac{1}{4} + 16\frac{2}{4} + 10\frac{1}{4} + 16\frac{2}{4}$$

$$= 52\frac{6}{4} = 52 + 1\frac{2}{4} = 53\frac{1}{2} \text{ feet}$$

881. She has 52 four-button dresses.

My calculation: That's roughly 50 four-button dresses. Fifty times four equals 200.   A) 200

882. Convert 275 minutes into hours and minutes.

$$60)\overline{275} \quad {}^{4\ R\ 35} \qquad \text{It will take Pat 4 hours and 35 minutes.}$$

885. If I have a quadrilateral in which all the vertices are right angles, must it be a rectangle?

Yes.

889. Which is smaller? $\frac{4}{7}$ or $\frac{5}{8}$

$$\frac{4}{7} = \frac{32}{56}$$

$$\frac{5}{8} = \frac{35}{56} \qquad \frac{4}{7} < \frac{5}{8}$$

890. Subtract seven-hundredths from three-tenths.

$$\frac{3}{10} - \frac{7}{100}$$

The LCM of the denominators is 100.

Multiply the top and bottom of the first fraction by 10.

$$\frac{30}{100} - \frac{7}{100} = \frac{23}{100}$$

891. A pentagon has five sides and five vertices. Is it possible for a pentagon to have four right angles?

I don't think so. Whenever I try to draw the first four angles as right angles, I can't turn it into a pentagon. Sometimes I end up with a rectangle and sometimes I end up with parallel lines that don't meet to form the fifth vertex.

my attempts

895. What is the square of $3\frac{1}{3}$?

The square of $3\frac{1}{3} = 3\frac{1}{3} \times 3\frac{1}{3} = \frac{10}{3} \times \frac{10}{3} = \frac{100}{9}$

$$= 9\overline{)100}^{\,11\ R\ 1} \qquad = 11\frac{1}{9}$$

900. If regular jelly beans cost 7 cents each, and if Texas-sized jelly beans cost 38 times as much, how much would a Texas-sized jelly bean cost?

It would cost 266 cents. (7×38)

903. If Joe's shirt weighed $500 \frac{1}{6}$ grams with the jelly bean drool on it, how much would it weigh after the ants removed the $12 \frac{3}{4}$ grams of jelly bean drool?

$$500 \frac{1}{6} = 500 \frac{4}{24} = 499 \frac{24}{24} + \frac{4}{24} = 499 \frac{28}{24}$$
$$- \quad 12 \frac{3}{4} = 12 \frac{18}{24} \qquad\qquad\qquad = 12 \frac{18}{24}$$
$$\overline{\qquad\qquad\qquad\qquad\qquad\qquad\qquad 487 \frac{10}{24} = 487 \frac{5}{12}}$$

Joe's shirt would weigh $487 \frac{5}{12}$ grams.

905. Four-fifths of Joe's diet comes from sugar. Draw a rectangle and color in four-fifths of it.

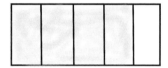

909. What is the square root of $11 \frac{1}{9}$?

In the previous problem (#895), you found that the square of $3 \frac{1}{3}$ was equal to $11 \frac{1}{9}$

Since taking a square root and finding a square are opposite operations, the square root of $11 \frac{1}{9}$ is equal to $3 \frac{1}{3}$

915. 68×78

$$\begin{array}{r} 68 \\ \times\ 78 \\ \hline 544 \\ 476 \\ \hline 5304 \end{array}$$

161

917. They paid him 6¢ for every 4 words. His article was 166 words long. How much was he paid?

This time I didn't warn you that this was a conversion factor problem. In Real Life you probably won't see a sign saying . . .

NOTICE
Hey! This is a conversion factor problem!

Step 1: You know that 6¢ = 4 words.

Step 2: The conversion factor will be either $\dfrac{6¢}{4\text{ words}}$ or $\dfrac{4\text{ words}}{6¢}$

Step 3: You are given 166 words.
You want to convert that to cents.

Step 4: $\dfrac{166\text{ words}}{1} \times \dfrac{6¢}{4\text{ words}} = \dfrac{166\text{ words}}{1} \times \dfrac{6¢}{4\text{ words}} =$

$= \dfrac{996¢}{4} = 4)\overline{996} \quad$ He was paid 249¢ (which is $2.49).

$\dfrac{249}{4)\overline{996}}$

918. Joe's comb had 65 teeth. After he scaled his fish he noticed that he had lost two-fifths of the teeth in his comb. How many teeth remained?

Two-fifths of 65 $= \dfrac{2}{5} \times \dfrac{65}{1} = \dfrac{2}{5} \times \dfrac{65^{13}}{1} = 26$

He lost 26 teeth in his comb.

Since he started with 65 teeth, 39 teeth remained (65 – 26 = 39).

A second way to do this problem:

If he lost $\dfrac{2}{5}$ of the teeth in his comb, then $\dfrac{3}{5}$ of the teeth remained.

$\dfrac{3}{5} \times \dfrac{65}{1} = \dfrac{3}{5} \times \dfrac{65^{13}}{1} = 39$ teeth remained.

920. Write three millionths as a fraction.

$\dfrac{3}{1,000,000}$

926. Is it possible for a pentagon to have three right angles?

That's easy to do.

935.   100 is "one hundred."

How would you say 644?   *Six hundred forty-four*
You don't say "and"

How would you say 5,000,733?   *Five million, seven hundred thirty-three*
Note the comma

How would you say 2,920?   *Two thousand, nine hundred twenty*
Note the comma

939. Darlene made a budget for her wedding. She planned on spending one-half on her dress, one-third on food, and one-sixth on flowers. How much did she have left over to spend on a wedding present for Joe?

$$\frac{1}{2} + \frac{1}{3} + \frac{1}{6}$$

$$= \frac{3}{6} + \frac{2}{6} + \frac{1}{6} = \frac{6}{6} \qquad \frac{6}{6} = 1 \text{ by General Rule \#3}$$ (Any fraction
where the top and bottom are equal to each other is equal to one.)

That means that Darlene will be spending all of her wedding money on her dress, food, and flowers. That leaves nothing for a wedding present for Joe.

940. In response to Darlene's "I read those bridal magazines because I hope, some day, to become a bride. Isn't that obvious?" Joe might have held up his copy of AMERICAN JELLY BEAN and said, "If reading bridal magazines means that you want to become a bride, then my reading AMERICAN JELLY BEAN means that I want to become a jelly bean."

942. SUPER SoFt MoUSe ShoeS MaDe FRoM CaT FUR. ONLY $4 eaCh. Joe sent in $8.

He should have sent in $16. (Mice have four feet.)

 Complete Solutions and Answers

943. Fill in one word: In an improper fraction the _numerator_ is greater than or equal to the denominator.

You could also written: In an improper fraction the _top_ is greater than or equal to the denominator.

$\frac{25}{9}$ is an improper fraction. So is $\frac{537}{537}$

945. What is the smallest cardinal number?

The cardinal numbers are the numbers we use to count things. For example, the set {✻, ☎, ✐, ❤} has a cardinal number of 4.

The number of men that Darlene wants to marry has a cardinal number of 1. The cardinal number of {Joe} is 1.

Is 1 the smallest cardinal number? No.

Consider the number of women that Joe is currently thinking of marrying. The cardinal number of { } is zero. That's the smallest cardinal number.

947. What do you call a regular quadrilateral?

It's going to have four sides since it is a quadrilateral.
All the sides will be equal since it is regular.
All the angles will be equal since it is regular.

It's a square.

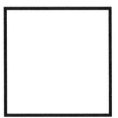

950.

$$\frac{\frac{5}{6}}{\frac{4}{5}} = \frac{5}{6} \div \frac{4}{5} = \frac{5}{6} \times \frac{5}{4} = \frac{25}{24} = 1\frac{1}{24}$$

These are secret pages.
Many readers will never
notice that they are
inserted here.

These pages contain one special HARD
fractions problem. It is a problem that is so
difficult that maybe only one reader in a
hundred will be able to solve it in under an
hour.

This problem doesn't take a lot of computation. It's not like figuring out $\frac{13}{237} + \frac{53}{391}$

That problem is long and boring. But not hard.*

This special hard problem is not hard to understand. It is just hard to figure out the answer.

This special problem is not a "trick" question. It just involves what you know already.

---

* I don't have many footnotes in this book, but this is a good spot for one. I wrote "But not hard." Those readers who know English would say that that is just a part of a sentence—known as **a sentence fragment**. When I was a high school student, one of my teachers would flunk any essay that we wrote that contained a sentence fragment.

All the other English teachers called these parts of a sentence "sentence fragments," but she called them fragmentary sentences. She was a tough teacher—and I learned a lot from her.

The usual kind of sentence fragment would be: *Because it was raining.*"

On the other hand, "But not hard" is called an **elliptical construction**. In an elliptical construction one or more words have been omitted. If I write *I can eat more pizza than you*, this is not a sentence fragment. It is an elliptical construction because I left out some words. The full sentence would read, *I can eat more pizza than you can eat.*

But not hard has words left out. With all the words inserted, it would read *But it is not hard.* This is not a sentence fragment, and my English teacher couldn't flunk my book!

This is the only problem in this book that I don't give the answer. You won't have the easy path of just reading the problem and then reading my answer. That would spoil all the fun.

If you spend a couple of years playing with it, that's okay. Once you find the answer, you will probably say to yourself, "That's so simple. Why didn't I think of that?"

Are you ready? ☐ Yes ☐ No

Once upon a time, Darlene was taking five classes at KITTENS University. She could count them on her fingers. She was taking English, life drawing, auto shop, history, and fractions.

Auto shop? The reason she was taking these five classes was that those were the classes that Joe was taking. She wanted to sit next to him in each class.

At the beginning of each semester she would ask Joe what he was taking. He wrote to her:

Dear Darlen,

This semester I'm taking five classes. English, life drawing, atu shop, history, and fractions. Five

Joe.

Darlene knew that that letter was really from Joe. He couldn't even spell her name right, and who else would need to illustrate the number five with a finger-painted handprint? Who else puts a period after their signature?

If you have read *Zillions of Praction Problems Fractions*, you know that Darlene spends a lot of her time painting her nails, thinking of about getting Joe to marry her, dreaming about her wedding (not *their* wedding), and going on Joe's boat while he goes fishing.

The number of hours each week that she spends studying is the same as the smallest cardinal number. (See problem #945 on page 72, if you have forgotten what the smallest cardinal number is.)

If you want success in what you are doing, there are two things that are essential. (see next page)

166

Two Keys to Success

1. Be interested in what you are doing.

2. Spend a lot of time doing it.

Darlene certainly wasn't spending a lot of time studying. And she certainly wasn't interested in auto shop. She couldn't tell the difference between a crankshaft and a carburetor.

As a result, Darlene was in danger of getting F's in all her five classes. If she flunked out of college, she wouldn't be able to be with Joe.

Intermission

Some kids head off to college rather than stay at home and go to classes. Their home might be in Kansas, and they head off to college in Florida.

It's their first taste of being away from home and being away from their parents.

At many universities . . .

1. They don't take attendance. Few know—or care—whether students to go to class.

2. The only tests are a midterm exam and the final exam. No weekly quizzes.

3. No one asks, "Have you done your homework?"

Every fall there are some students who spend every afternoon and evening with their friends having a "good time."

In the spring they are working at a fast food place. They are no longer in college.

Darlene had two choices: ① She could get interested in her classes and study or ② She could try to bribe her teachers.

She decided on ②. She would bake her famous peanut butter cookies for her five teachers. That would take less time than studying.

"And besides," she thought to herself, "making giant peanut butter cookies is duck soup.*"

Mix a half cup of butter, a cup of sugar, an egg, a cup of peanut butter, a little salt, a little baking soda, a half teaspoon of vanilla, and a cup of flour. Roll it into five big balls on cookie sheets and smash it down a bit with a fork to make them into fat pancakes. Bake 375°.

When Darlene's mom had made them for Darlene when Darlene was a little kid, the cookies were warm and soft. Darlene was sure that her teachers would like the cookies.

There was only one slight problem with those five cookies that Darlene made. She had baked them for an hour. (Peanut butter cookies usually take about ten minutes in the oven.)

Instead of being soft, they were brittle. You could cut them, for example, into quarters and there wouldn't be a problem.

But any less than a quarter and the cookie would fall into crumbles.

---

* Duck soup? That means the same as it's a breeze or it's a piece of cake or a picnic or a pushover or a snap or it's as easy as falling off a log or it's a cinch.

  Duck soup is such a weird phrase. You might be interested in its **etymology** (where the phrase came from). That's a tough question. Etymologists have traced its first use back to a 1902 newspaper cartoon in which a man is juggling a bottle, a pitcher, a plate, and a salt shaker. The caption under the drawing was "Duck Soup." That was total nonsense.

  The phrase became really popular as the title of a Marx Brothers movie in 1933. The movie has nothing to do with either ducks or soup.

"No problem" thought Darlene. "They may be a little burned, but my teachers will know that my intentions are good."

Joe showed up in Darlene's kitchen when the cookies came out of the oven. He was always there when cookies were fresh baked.

"Sorry, Joe. You can't have any of these. These peanut butter cookies are for our five teachers. You know, for our classes in English, life drawing, auto shop, history, and fractions."

"You forgot our biology class" Joe told her.

"Biology! I had completely forgotten about that class."

Six classes. Six teachers. Five cookies.

How much should each teacher get? That's an easy question. Anyone who's read *Life of Fred: Fractions* knows that each teacher will get $\frac{5}{6}$ of a cookie.

Joe's solution was to cut each cookie into six pieces. With five cookies, that would make 30 pieces, and each teacher would get five pieces. But that wouldn't work because $\frac{1}{6} < \frac{1}{4}$ and everything would be in crumbles.

The HARD question—the one that you have been waiting for—is: How to cut the five cookies so that each teacher will receive $\frac{5}{6}$ of a cookie and none of them will get crumbles?

Index

Index

Index

Index